ANDREW LLOYD WEBBER

GOLD

REQUIEM

THIS PUBLICATION IS NOT AUTHORISED
FOR SALE IN THE UNITED STATES OF AMERICA
AND/OR CANADA.

A REALLY USEFUL GROUP PUBLICATION
WWW.REALLYUSEFUL.COM

EXCLUSIVE DISTRIBUTORS:
MUSIC SALES LIMITED
8/9 FRITH STREET, LONDON W1B 3JB, ENGLAND.
MUSIC SALES PTY LIMITED
120 ROTHSCHILD AVENUE, ROSEBERY, NSW 2018, AUSTRALIA.

WWW.MUSICSALES.COM

ORDER NO. RUG37488
ISBN 0-7119-9295-9

MUSIC PROCESSED BY DAKOTA MUSIC SERVICE.
COVER ARTWORK COURTESY OF REALLY USEFUL RECORDS.

PRINTED IN THE UNITED KINGDOM BY
CALIGRAVING LIMITED, THETFORD, NORFOLK.

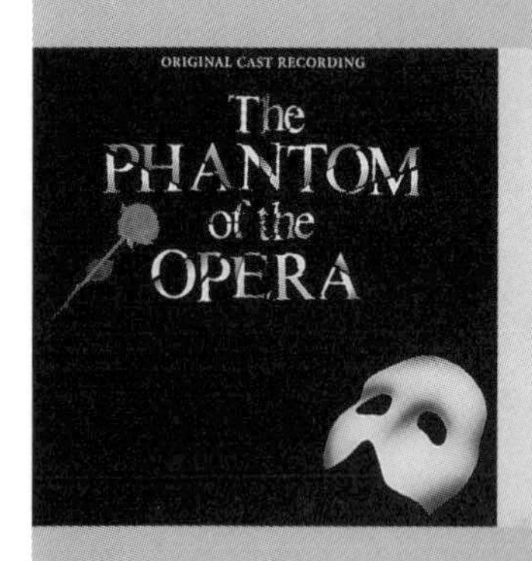

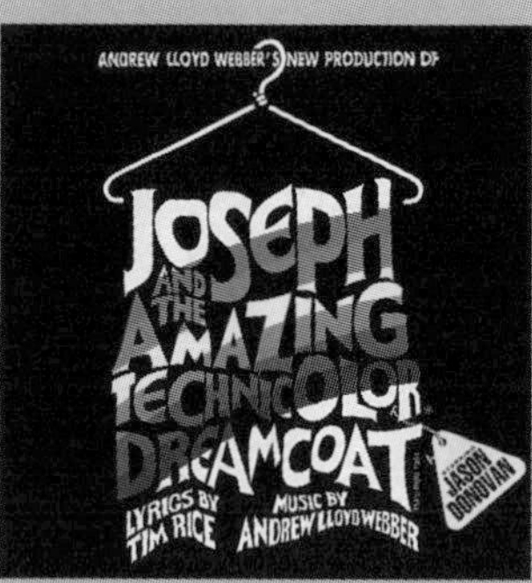

A REALLY USEFUL GROUP PUBLICATION
WWW.REALLYUSEFUL.COM

SUPERSTAR

YVONNE ELLIMAN
I Don't Know How
To Love Him
c/w Overture MKS 5063
FROM THE ROCK OPERA
JESUS CHRIST SUPERSTAR
ANDREW LLOYD WEBBER
DON BLACK
Tell me on a Sunday
MARTI WEBB
TAKE THAT LOOK OFF YOUR FACE

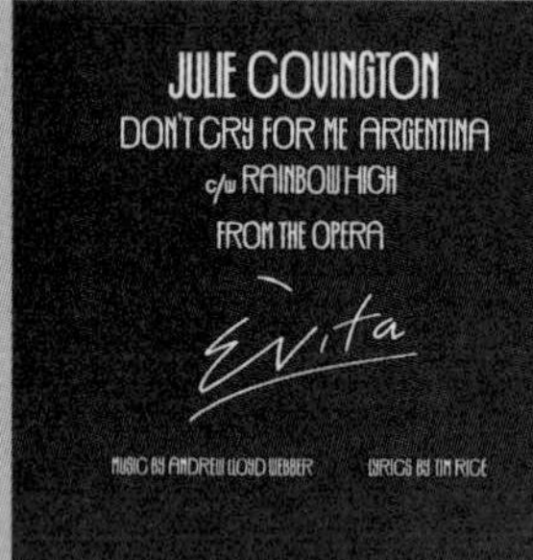
JULIE COVINGTON
DON'T CRY FOR ME ARGENTINA
c/w RAINBOW HIGH
FROM THE OPERA
Evita
MUSIC BY ANDREW LLOYD WEBBER
LYRICS BY TIM RICE
MCA RECORDS

BARBARA DICKSON
ANOTHER SUITCASE IN ANOTHER HALL
c/w
REQUIEM FOR EVITA
FROM THE OPERA
Evita
MUSIC BY ANDREW LLOYD WEBBER
LYRICS BY TIM RICE
MCA RECORDS
MCA 856

Pie Jesu
FROM
ANDREW LLOYD WEBBER'S
REQUIEM
SARAH BRIGHTMAN
and
PAUL MILES-KINGSTON
Save the Children

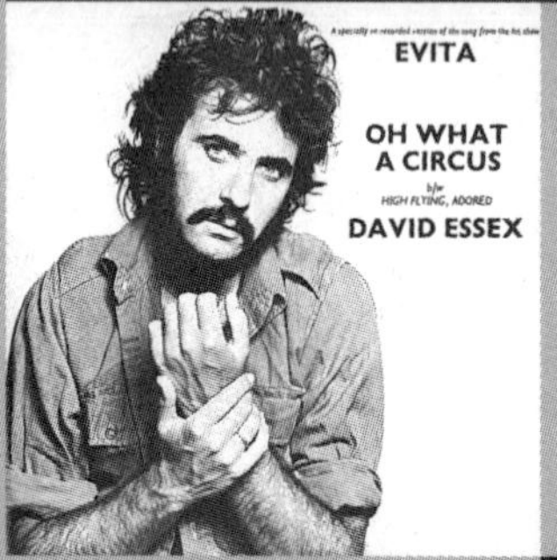
EVITA
OH WHAT
A CIRCUS
b/w
HIGH FLYING, ADORED
DAVID ESSEX

'MEMORY'
THE THEME FROM
CATS
SUNG BY
ELAINE PAIGE

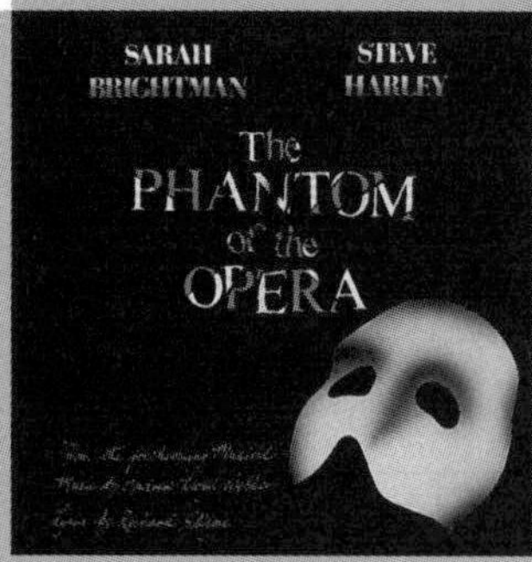
SARAH
BRIGHTMAN
STEVE
HARLEY
The
PHANTOM
of the
OPERA

"Love Changes Everything"
Aspects of Love

BARBRA STREISAND
As If We Never Said Goodbye
(from Sunset Boulevard)

jason donovan
ANY DREAM WILL DO

FROM

JOSÉ CARRERAS
SARAH BRIGHTMAN
ANDREW
LLOYD WEBBER'S
Amigos
Para Siempre
(FRIENDS FOR LIFE)
THE
OFFICIAL THEME
OF
THE BARCELONA
1992 GAMES

The
PHANTOM
of the
OPERA
Special
Edition
MICHAEL CRAWFORD
'The Music of the Night'
SARAH BRIGHTMAN
'Wishing You Were Somehow Here Again'
ALL TITLES FROM THE FORTHCOMING ORIGINAL CAST ALBUM

Tina Arena
WHISTLE
down the
WIND
from Andrew Lloyd Webber
and Jim Steinman's new musical

Cliff Richard
Sarah Brightman
'All I Ask Of You'
Music by ANDREW LLOYD WEBBER
Lyrics by CHARLES HART
From the Musical The Phantom of the Opera

DINA CARROLL
THE PERFECT YEAR

boyzone no matter what

MADONNA
YOU
MUST
LOVE
ME
EVITA

JESUS CHRIST SUPERSTAR

The PHANTOM of the OPERA

SUPERSTAR

MUSIC BY ANDREW LLOYD WEBBER
LYRICS BY TIM RICE

Maestoso
E
A/E
D/E
A/E
ff
E
A/E
D/E
A/E
E
a tempo — Lively rock
E
Ev - 'ry time I look at you I
Tell me what you think a - bout your
f
G6
don't un - der - stand,
friends at the top,
A7
why you let the things you did get
who d'you think be - sides your - self's the

E
so out of hand.
pick of the crop?
You'd have man - aged bet - ter if you'd
Bud - dha, was he where it's at? Is
G6
had it planned.
he where you are?
A7
Why'd you choose such a back - ward time and
Could Ma - ho - met move a moun - tain or
E
such a strange land?
was that just P. R.
If you'd come to - day you would have
Did you mean to die like that? Was
G
reached a whole na - tion,
that a mis - take or
A7
Is - rael in Four B. C. had no
did you know your mes - sy death would

E
(Don't you get me wrong)
(don't you get me
mass com - mu - ni - ca - tion.
Don't you get me wrong,
be a re - cord brea - ker?
G
A7
wrong now)
(don't you get me wrong)
(don't you get me
don't you get me wrong,
don't you get me wrong,
E
wrong now)
(I on - ly want to know)
(I on - ly want to
don't you get me wrong,
on - ly want to know,
G
A
know now)
(I on - ly want to know)
(I on - ly want to
on - ly want to know,
on - ly want to know,

E E A
know now.)
on - ly want to know. Je - sus Christ, Je - sus Christ.
D A E A
Who are you? What have you sa - cri - ficed? Je - sus Christ, Je - sus Christ.
D A E A
Who are you? What have you sa - cri - ficed? Je - sus Christ, su - per - star,
D A E
do you think you're what they say you are? Je - sus Christ,

1.
A
D
A
E
E G A Adim E
su - per - star, do you think you're what they say you are?
G A Adim E G A Adim E E
Brass
2.
Repeat ad lib.
To Coda
E
A
D
A
E
Je - sus Christ, su - per - star, do you think you're what they say you are?
Coda
D
A/E
E
Are you what they say you are?
fff molto rall.

I DON'T KNOW HOW TO LOVE HIM

MUSIC BY ANDREW LLOYD WEBBER
LYRICS BY TIM RICE

Slowly, tenderly and very expressively

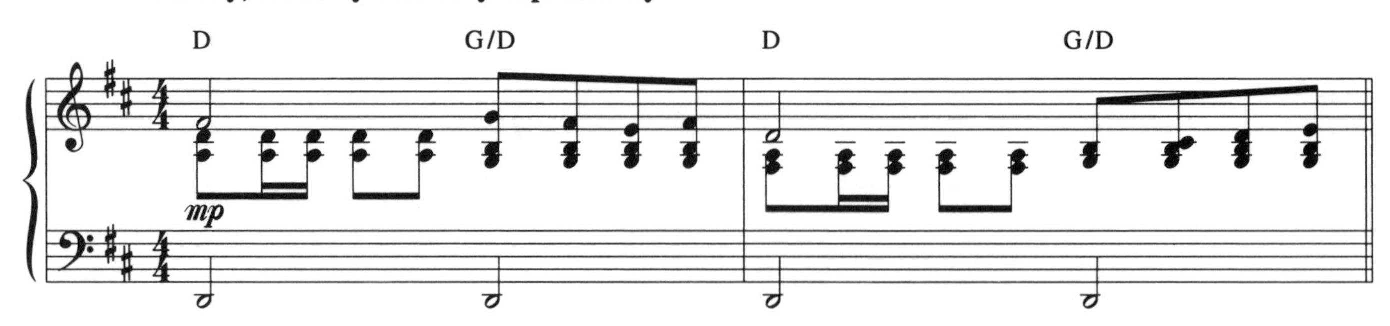

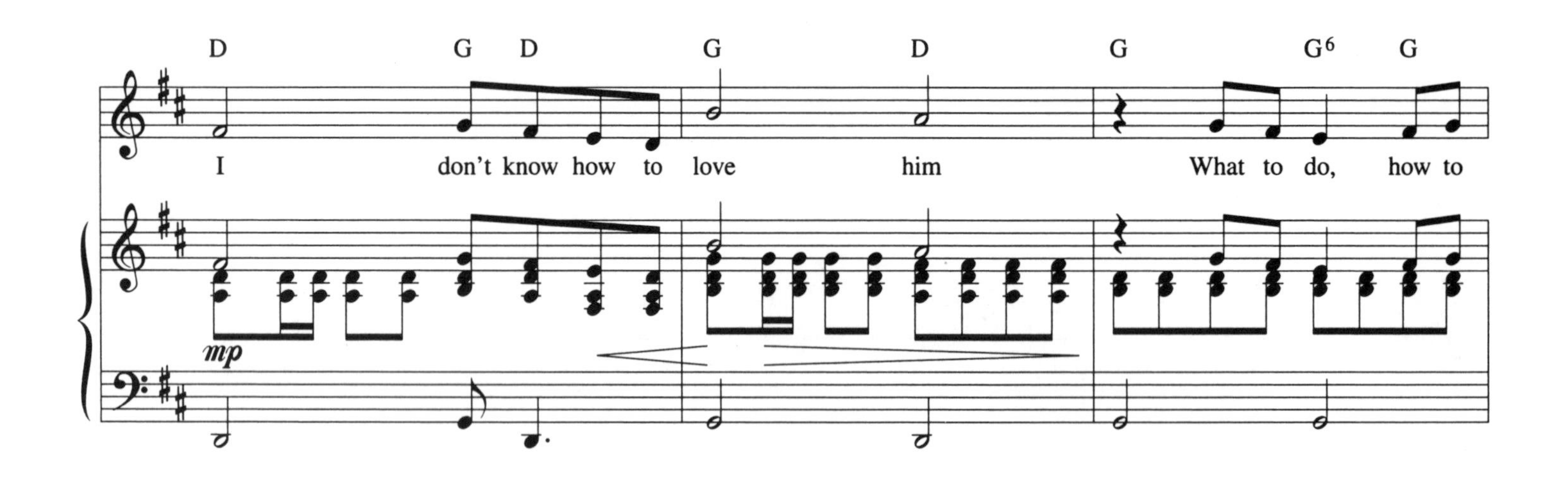

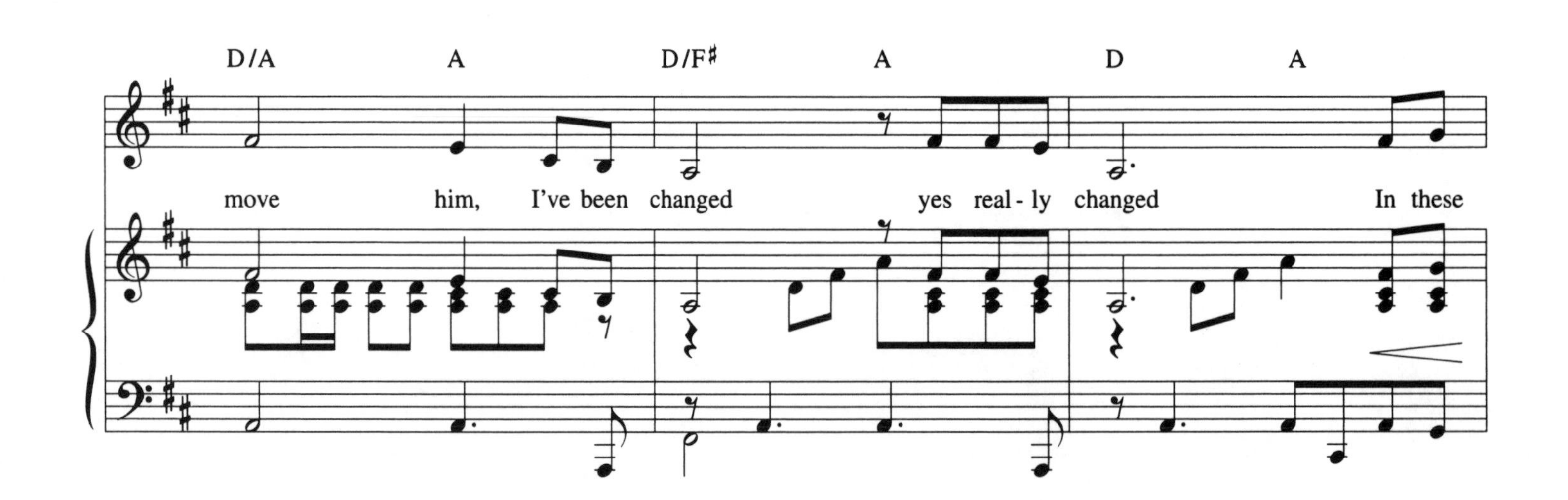

F♯m7 Bm F♯m7 Bm G D/F♯ Em D
past few days when I've seen my-self I seem like some-one
A add9 sus4 A D G D G D
else I don't know how to take this
G G6 G D/A A D/F♯ A
I don't see why he moves me, He's a man he's just a
D A F♯m7 Bm F♯m7 Bm
man And I've had so ma-ny men be-fore in

G D/F♯ Em D A add9 sus4 A G D/F♯ Em7 D
ve - ry ma - ny ways He's just one more.
p
(2º instrumental)
G F♯7 Bm Bm/A
Should I bring him down should I scream and shout Should I speak of love
mp
cresc. poco a poco
(Vocal each time)
G D/A C G D
let my feel- ings out? I ne - ver thought I'd come to this
ff
f dim. poco a poco
G D/F♯ Em A add9 sus4 A D G D
what's it all a - bout? Don't you think it's ra- ther
Yet if he said he
mp

G D G G6 G D/A A
fun - ny I should be in this po - si - - - tion? I'm the
loved me I'd be lost I'd be fright - - - ened I could-n't
D/F♯ A D A F♯m7 Bm7
one who's al - ways been So calm so cool
cope just could-n't cope I'd turn my head
F♯m7 Bm7 G D/F♯ Em D Asus4 A G D/F♯ Em7
no lo - ver's fool Run - ning ev - 'ry show He scares me
I'd back a - way I would - n't want to know He scares me
1. 2.
D D G D/F♯ Em7 D G D/F♯ Em7 D
so. so I want him so I love him so.
p
mp
mf

DON'T CRY FOR ME ARGENTINA

MUSIC BY ANDREW LLOYD WEBBER
LYRICS BY TIM RICE

Db
Gb/Db
Ab7/Db
Dbsus4
Db
Fm/C
Bbm
Bbm/Db
Ebsus4
Eb
Eb/Db
Ab/C
N.C.
Db
Gb/Db
It won't be ea - sy, you'll think it strange when I
mf
f
p

A♭7/D♭
3
try to ex-plain how I feel, that I still need your love af-ter
D♭
B♭m/D♭
all that I've done.
You won't be - lieve me.
E♭
E♭/D♭
3
All you will see is a girl you once knew, al-though she's dressed up to the
A♭/C
E♭
A♭
nines, at six - es and se - vens with you.
poco rall.

a tempo
D♭
G♭/D♭
I had to let it hap - pen, I had to change, could - n't
p
A♭7/D♭
spend all my life down at heel, look - ing out of the win - dow, stay - ing
D♭
B♭m/D♭
out of the sun. So I chose free - - dom,
E♭
E♭/D♭
run - ning a - round try - ing ev - 'ry - thing new, but no - thing im - pressed me at all, _

A♭/C
E♭
A♭
I ne - ver ex - pec - ted it to.
D♭
B♭m/D♭
Don't cry for me Ar - gen - ti - na, the truth is I ne - ver
D♭4 D♭
A♭
B♭m
left you. All through my wild days, my mad ex - is - tence, I kept my
D♭maj7
G♭maj7
G♭6 G♭
pro - mise, don't keep your dis - tance.

D♭
G♭/D♭
And as for for - tune and as for fame, I
A♭7/D♭
ne - ver in - vi - ted them in, though it seemed to the world they were
D♭
B♭m/D♭
all I de - sired. They are ill - u - - sions, they're
E♭
E♭/D♭
not the so - lu - tions they pro - mised to be, the an - swer was here all the

A♭/C
E♭
A♭
rall.
time, I love you and hope you love me.
rall.
N.C.
CHOIR -
bouche fermée
G♭maj7
Don't cry for me Ar - gen - ti - na. Mm
colla voce
p
E♭m7
D♭
A♭
B♭m
D♭maj7
G♭
EVA
D♭
Don't cry for me Ar - gen -

ti - na, the truth is I ne - ver left you. All through my
3
Ab7
Bbm
Dbmaj7
wild days, my mad ex - is - tence, I kept my pro - mise, don't keep your
Gbmaj7
colla voce
dis - tance. Have I said too much, there's no - thing more I can think of to
rall.
Fm7
Gbmaj7
say to you. But all you have to do is
tr

Db
look at me to know that ev - 'ry word is true.
timp.
ff
Db6
Db
Ab
Bbm
Dbmaj7
Gbmaj7
Gb6
Gbmaj7
Db
poco rit.
p

Andrew Lloyd Webber

Tim Rice

Evita

An opera
based on
the life story of
Eva Peron
1919-1952

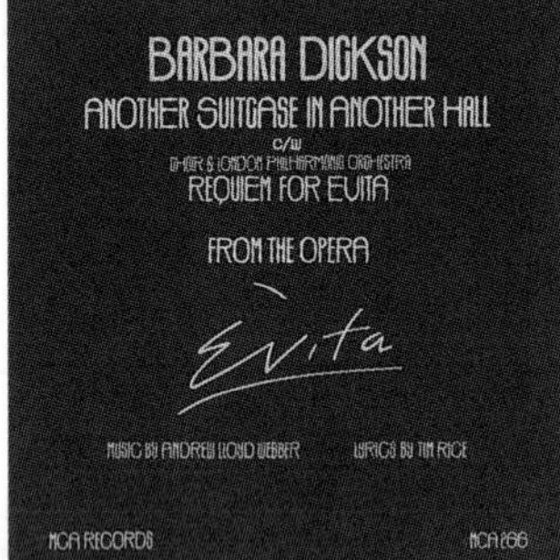

ANOTHER SUITCASE IN ANOTHER HALL

MUSIC BY ANDREW LLOYD WEBBER
LYRICS BY TIM RICE

C C7 C
Bb/C C Bb/C C Bb/C C
I
C F G7 C
don't ex - pect my love af - fairs to last for long, ne - ver
time and time a - gain I've said that I don't care that I'm im -
call in three months time and I'll be fine I know well
F C/E Dm G C G7
fool my - self that my dreams will come true.
mune to gloom, that I'm hard through and through but
may - be not that fine but I'll sur - vive an - y how, I

C
F
G
Am
Be - ing used to trou - ble I an - ti - - - ci - pate it but
ev - ery time it mat - ters all my words de - sert me so
won't re - call the names and plac - es of this sad oc - ca - sion, but

C/G
F
C
all the same I hate it would - n't you, so what hap - pens
an - y - one can hurt me, and they do, so what hap - pens
that's no con - so - la - tion here and now, so what hap - pens

G
C
G
C
now, so what hap - pens now? Where am I
CHOIR
An - oth - er suit - case in an - oth - er hall, take your pic - ture off an - oth - er wall.

1, 2.
F
Am
F
C/E Dm
go - ing to?
Where am I
go - ing to?
You'll get by you al - ways have be - fore.
C
C7
C
3.
F
C
C7
C
go - ing to?
Don't ask an - y more.

OH WHAT A CIRCUS

MUSIC BY ANDREW LLOYD WEBBER
LYRICS BY TIM RICE

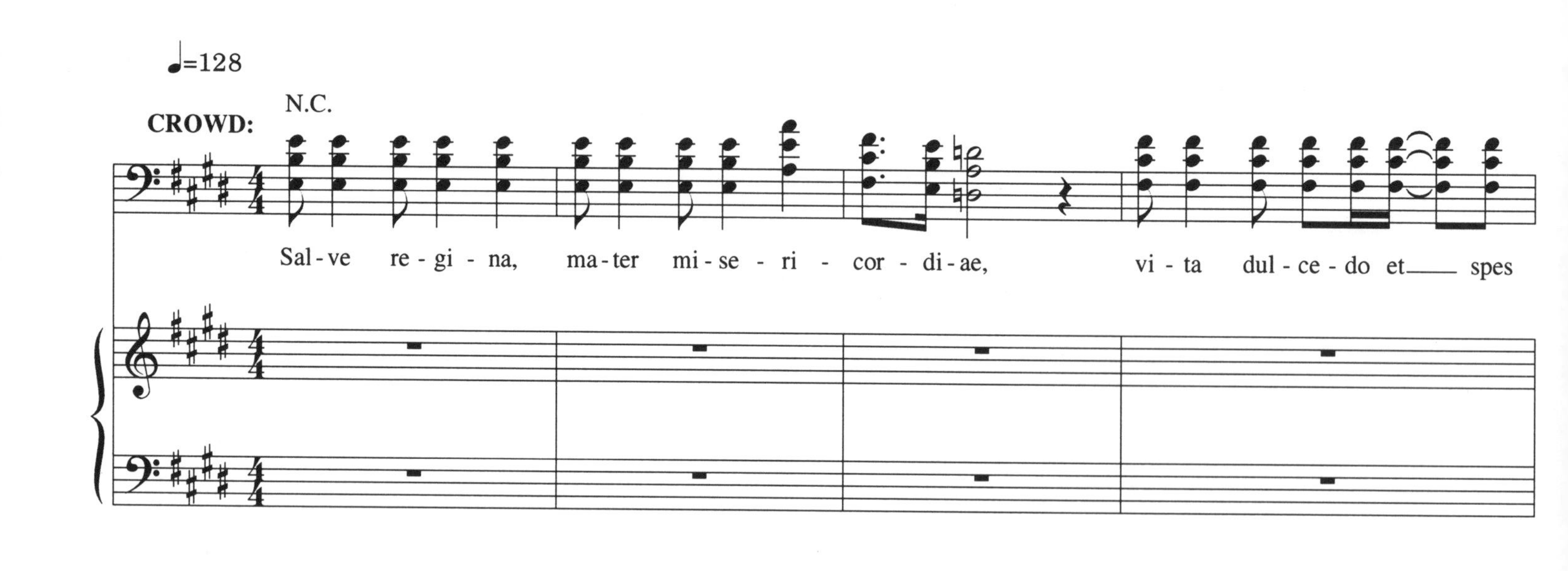

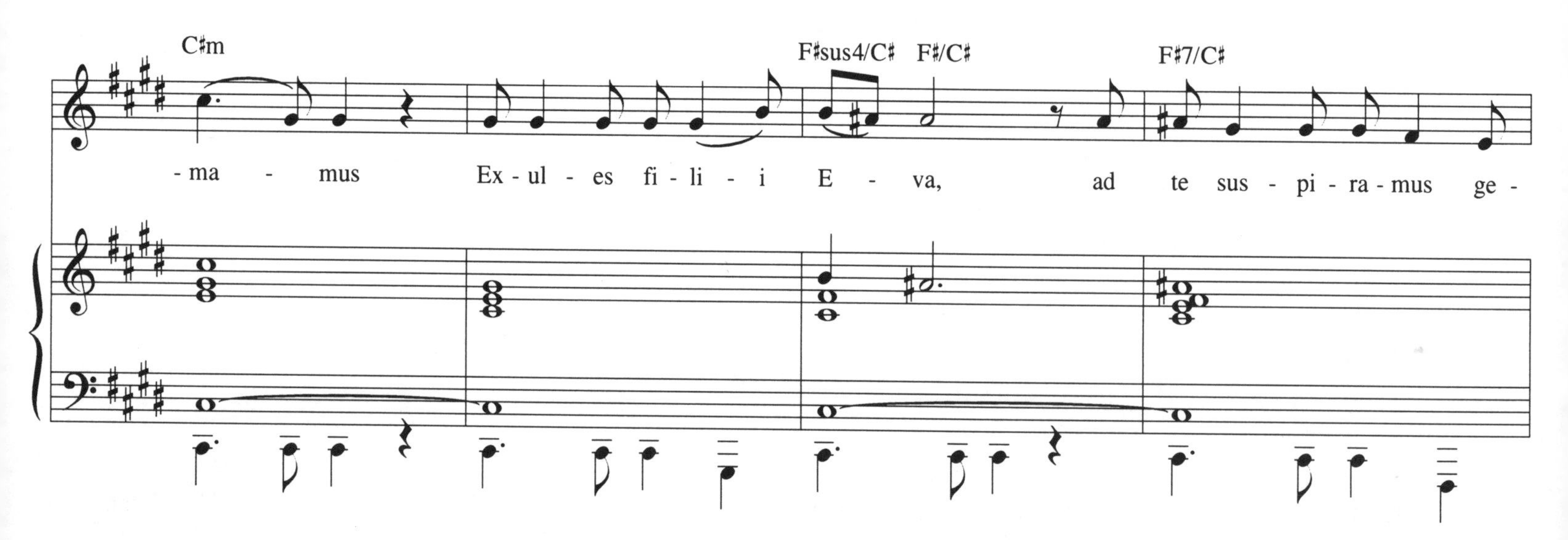

B/D♯
F♯/A♯
F♯7/A♯
B
-men - tes et flen - tes, O clem - ens, O pi - a.
E
CHE:
1. Oh, what a cir - cus! Oh, what a
(Verses 2, 3, 4, 5 see block lyric)
A
B
show! Ar - gen - ti - na has gone to town ov - er the
E
death of an act - ress called E - va Pe - ron. We've all gone

cra - - - zy, mourn - ing all day and all of the night, fall - ing
ov - er our - selves to get all
B
F#7
of the mis - er - y
1.
B7
right.
2.
B7
-day.
N.C.
But who is this San - ta E -
E
A/E
E
A/E
E
- vi - ta? Why all this howl - ing, hy - ster - ic - al sor - row? What kind of

B
C♯m
E
god - dess
has lived a - mong us?
How will we ev - er
get by with -

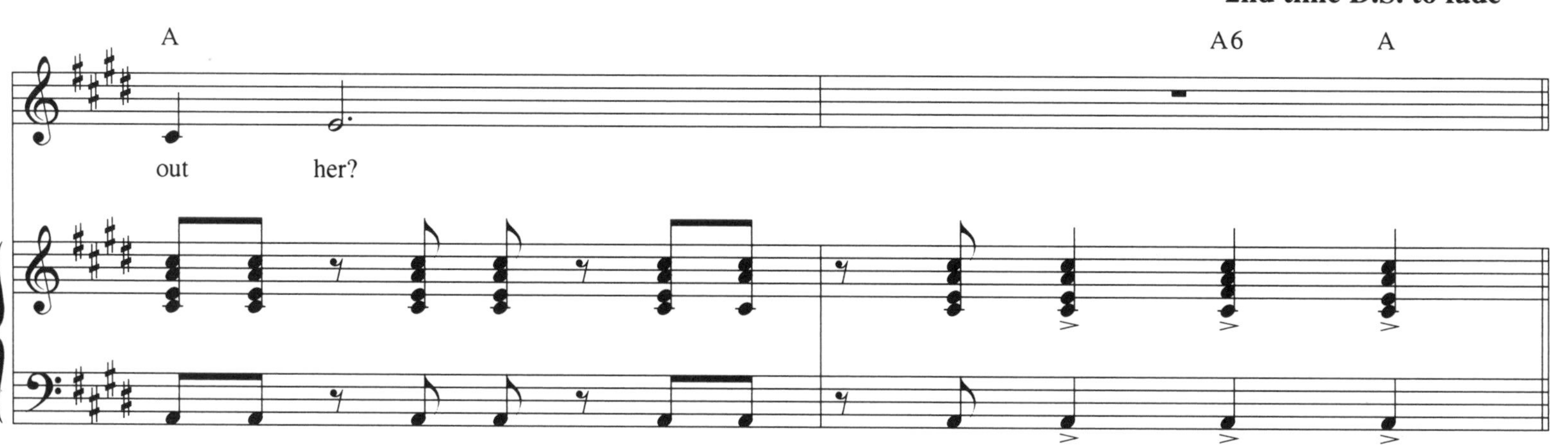
1st time D.S. (with rpt.)
2nd time D.S. to fade
A
A6
A
out her?

Verse 2

Oh, what an exit! That's how to go!
When they're ringing your curtain down
Demand to be buried like Eva Peron.
It's quite a sunset
And good for the country in a roundabout way
We've made the front pages of all the world's papers today!

Verse 3

Salve regina, mater misericordiae,
Vita dulcedo et spes nostra.
Salve, salve regina,
Ad te clamamus exules filii Eva,
Ad te suspiramus gementes et flentes
O clemens, O pia!

Verse 4

She had her moments, she had some style.
The best show in town was the crowd
Outside the Casa Rosada crying "Eva Peron".
But that's all gone now
As soon as the smoke from the funeral clears
We're all going to see - and how! - she did nothing for years.
You let down your people Evita
You were supposed to have been immortal
That's all they wanted
Not much to ask for
But in the end you could not deliver.

Verse 5

Salve regina, mater misericordiae,
Vita dulcedo et spes nostra.
Salve, salve regina,
Ad te clamamus exules filii Eva,
Ad te suspiramus gementes et flentes
O clemens, O pia! (Repeat)

TAKE THAT LOOK OFF YOUR FACE

MUSIC BY ANDREW LLOYD WEBBER
LYRICS BY DON BLACK

1.
2, 3.
G
G/A
D
hate it when he's a - way.
2. You know if he had - n't gone.
on - ly a wo - man can.
CHORUS
(B. Vocals)
Take that look off your face (Take that look off you face) I can
No I did - n't dig deep (No I did - n't dig deep) I did
A7
see thru' your smile (I can see thru' your smile) You would
not want to know (I did not want to know) Well you
love to be right, I bet you did - n't sleep good last night, could - n't wait to bring
don't in - ter - fere when you're scared of the things you might hear when he's back, you think
f
Ped.

G7
Bm
all of that bad news to my door. Well I've
I will end it right there and then. Well my
G
G D/F♯ Em7 D
1.
G/D D
got news for you I knew be-fore.
fair wea-ther friend you're wrong a-gain.
2.
D
Gadd A/D
3. If
(Take that
D
A7
look off your face) take that look off your face (I can
ff

A7
see thru' your smile_) I can see thru' your smile,_ you would
D
A7
love to be right,_ I bet you did-n't sleep good last night_ could-n't wait to bring
G7
Bm
G
all of that bad_ news to my door, well I've got news for you_
G D/F♯ Em7 D
G add A/D
Repeat to fade
I knew be-fore._ (Take that

MEMORY

MUSIC BY ANDREW LLOYD WEBBER
LYRICS BY TREVOR NUNN AFTER T.S. ELIOT

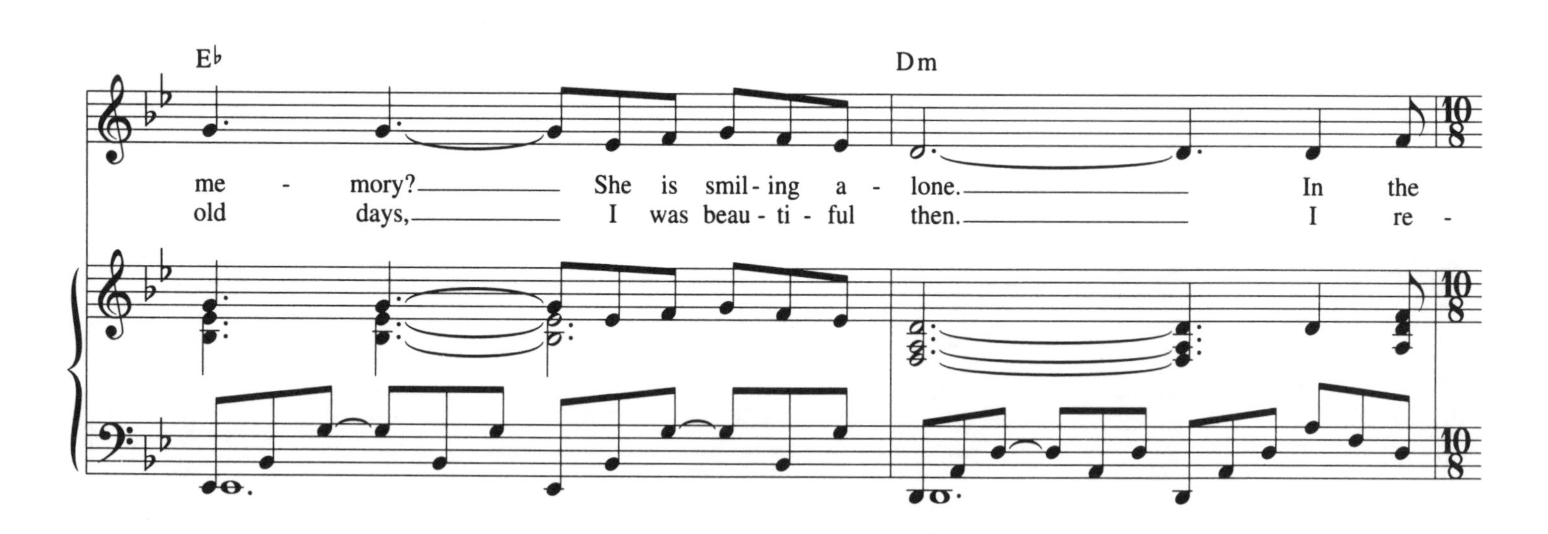

Cm
Gm
lamp - light the wi - thered leaves col - lect at my feet and the
mem - ber the time I knew what hap - pi - ness was, let the
1.
2.
F
E♭/F
B♭
wind be - gins to moan.
me - mory live a - gain.
Dm
Dm/E♭
Cm/E♭
Bbmaj7
C
Fmaj7
Ev - ery street lamp seems to beat a fa - ta - lis - tic warn - ing.
poco rit.
Gm7
C7
Dm/G
G7
Some - one mut - ters and a street lamp gut - ters and soon it will be morn - ing.

a tempo
B♭
Gm
E♭
Day - light. I must wait for the sun - rise, I must think of a new life and I must-n't give
Dm
Cm
Gm
in. When the dawn comes to-night will be a me-mo-ry too and a
F
E♭/F
B♭
G♭
new day will be - gin.
E♭m
C♭
B♭m

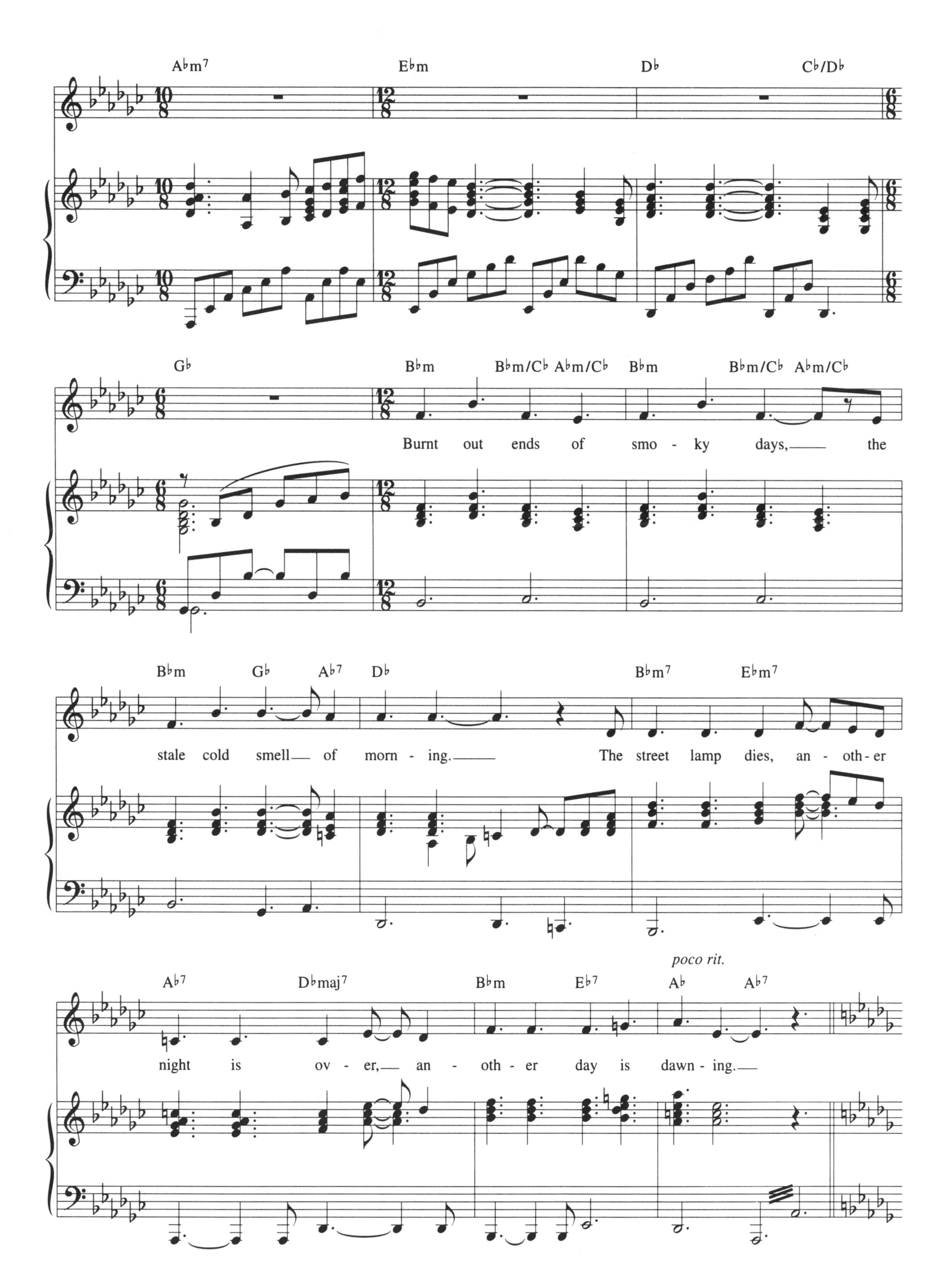
A♭m7
E♭m
D♭
C♭/D♭
G♭
B♭m
B♭m/C♭
A♭m/C♭
B♭m
B♭m/C♭
A♭m/C♭
Burnt out ends of smo - ky days, the
B♭m
G♭
A♭7
D♭
B♭m7
E♭m7
stale cold smell of morn - ing.
The street lamp dies, an - oth - er
poco rit.
A♭7
D♭maj7
B♭m
E♭7
A♭
A♭7
night is ov - er, an - oth - er day is dawn - ing.

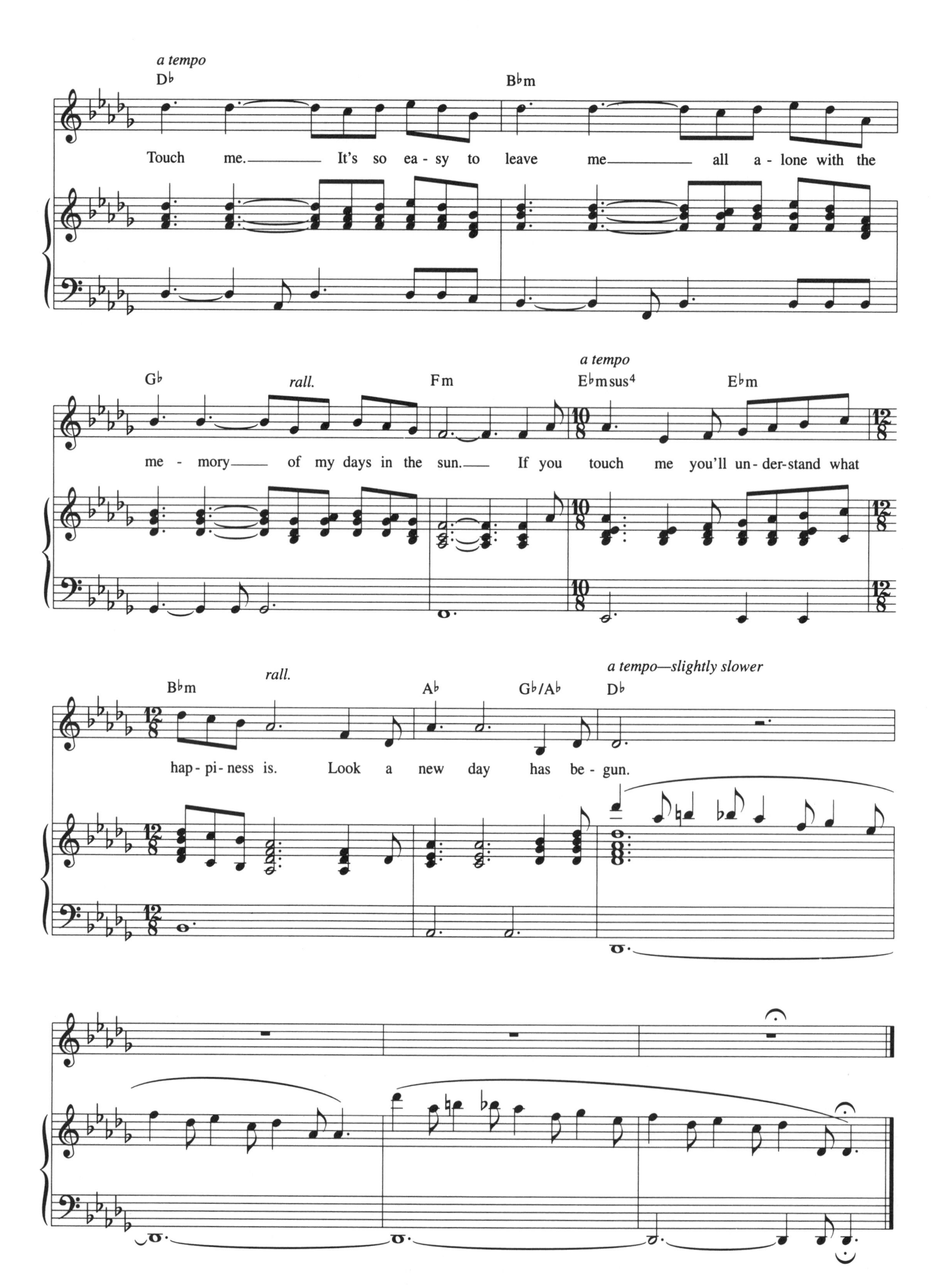

a tempo
D♭
B♭m
Touch me. It's so ea-sy to leave me all a-lone with the
G♭
rall.
Fm
a tempo
E♭msus4
E♭m
me-mory of my days in the sun. If you touch me you'll un-der-stand what
B♭m
rall.
A♭
G♭/A♭
a tempo—slightly slower
D♭
hap-pi-ness is. Look a new day has be-gun.

PIE JESU

MUSIC BY ANDREW LLOYD WEBBER

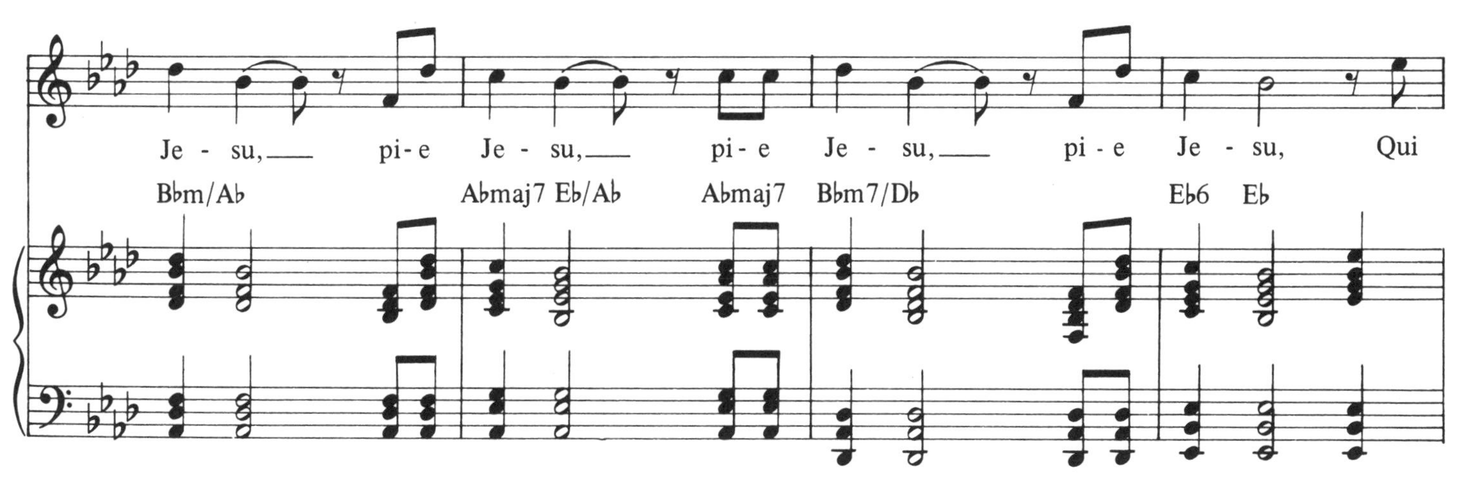

re-qui-em.
SOLO BOY
mp
Pi-e Je - su, pi-e Je - su, pi-e
Ab
Bbm/Ab
Eb7/Ab
Ab
Qui tol - lis pec-ca-ta mun-di,
Je - su, pi-e Je - su, Qui tol - lis pec-ca-ta mun-di,
SOPRANO
p
ALTO
Hm
TENOR
BASS
p
Bbm7/Db
Eb7
Db
Eb

Do-na e-is re-qui-em do-na e - is re-qui-em.
Do-na e-is re-qui-em, do-na e - is re-qui-em.
Hm
Ab Fm Bbm7 Eb7 Ab Abmaj7
mf
Ag-nus De - i, Ag-nus
Ag-nus De - i, Ag-nus
Ag-nus De - i, Ag-nus
Ab6 Ab Dbmaj7 Db/Eb Cm/Eb Bbm7/Ab

De - i, Ag-nus De - i, Ag-nus De - i, Qui
De - i, Ag-nus De - i, Ag-nus De - i, Qui
De - i, Ag-nus De - i, Ag-nus De - i.
Eb7 Ab/Eb Bbm7/Ab Eb7
tol - lis pec - ca - ta mun - di, do - na e - is re - qui-em,
tol - lis pec - ca - ta mun - di, do - na e - is re - qui-em,
Db Eb7/Db Ab/C Fm

mp
do - na e - is re - qui - em sem - pi -
mp
do - na e - is re - qui - em sem - pi -
do - na e - is re - qui - em,
p
Bbm7 Eb7 Ab Abmaj7
mp
rall.
p
pp
slow
ter - nam, sem- pi - ter - nam, re - qui - em.
p
pp
ter - nam, sem- pi - ter - nam, sem- pi - ter - nam.
do - na e - is re - qui - em.
rall.
slow
Ab6 Ab Db Bbm7 Eb7 Db/Ab Bbm/Ab Ab
pp

THE PHANTOM OF THE OPERA

MUSIC BY ANDREW LLOYD WEBBER
LYRICS BY CHARLES HART
ADDITIONAL LYRICS BY RICHARD STILGOE & MIKE BATT

C
Dm
Bbmaj7
Bb6
C
he's ev - 'ry - where.
And when my song be - gins,
I al - ways
Dm
Dm
find
the Phan - tom of the Op - e - ra is
Bbdim
Dm
Dbm
Cm
B
there
in - side my mind.
Bb
Ab
Bb
Gm
PHANTOM:
Sing once a -

Csus4
Cm
F
Gm
Csus4
Cm
-gain with me our strange du - et; my pow - er ov - er you
F
Gm
E♭maj7
E♭6
grows strong - er yet. You'll give your love to me,
F
Gm
Gm
for love is blind. The Phan -
Cdim
F♯dim
Gm
- tom of the Op - e - ra is now your mast - er mind.

Gbm
Fm
Em
Eb
D
D7
Em
Am
D
Em/B
KRISTIN:
Those who have seen your face draw back in fear; I am the
Am
D
PHANTOM:
Em
BOTH:
mask you wear, it's me they hear.
Your
my
spi - rit
Cmaj7
C6
D
Em
Em
and your
my
voice in one com - bined. The Phan -

Cdim
Em
– tom of the Op-e-ra is there in-side your mind
my
C
Fm
Eb
Fm
BOTH:
Db
Sing once a-gain with me
Eb
Fm
PHANTOM:
Db
Eb
our strange du-et; my pow-er ov-er you grows strong-er
8va basso
Fm
BOTH:
Db
Eb
Fm
yet. You'll give your love to me for love is blind.
8va basso

Fm
D♭dim
The Phantom - tom of the Op - e - ra is now
8va basso
Fm
D♭
PHANTOM:
KRISTIN:
your / my mas - ter mind.
Sing my angel of music
He's
3
8va basso
Fm
D♭
there, the Phan - tom of the Op - e - ra.
Fm
D♭
Ah.
Sing once again with me our strange duet;
my power over you
PHANTOM:

PHANTOM: *Continue over Fade*

The Phantom of the Opera
Is now your mastermind;
I am here
Inside your mind.
I am everywhere,
You're in my power.
Sing,
Sing, my angel of music,
Sing. . . .

ALL I ASK OF YOU

MUSIC BY ANDREW LLOYD WEBBER
LYRICS BY CHARLES HART
ADDITIONAL LYRICS BY RICHARD STILGOE

Andante
RAOUL
D♭
No more talk of dark- ness, for - get these wide- eyed fears: I'm
mp
D♭maj7
G♭6/D♭
C♭
A♭/C
here, noth- ing can harm you, my words will warm and calm you.
D♭
Let me be your free - dom, let day - light dry your tears: I'm

Dbmaj7 Gb6 Cb Ab/C
here, with you, be- side you, to guard you and to guide you.
Db Bbm7 Ebm7 Ab Db/F Bbm7
CHRISTINE
Say you love me ev- ery wak - ing mo- ment, turn my head with talk of
Ebm7 Ebm7/Ab Db Bbm7 Ebm7 Ab
sum- mer- time. Say you need me with you now and al- ways;
Db/F Gb Db/Ab rit. Ebm/Ab Ab6 Ebm7/Ab
pro- mise me that all you say is true, that's all I ask of

a tempo
RAOUL
Db
Dbmaj7
Gb6
Let me be your shel- ter, let me be your light; you're safe, no- one will find you your
you.
mf
CHRISTINE
Cb
Ab/C
Db
fears are far be- hind you. All I want is free- dom, a world with no more night; and
Dbmaj7
Gb6
Cb
Ab/C
RAOUL
Db
Bbm7
you, al- ways be- side me, to hold me and to hide me. Then say you'll share with me one
f
Ebm7
Ab
Db/F
Bbm7
Ebm7
G/Ab Ab Ab6 Ab7
love, on life- time; let me lead you from your so- li- tude.

Db Bbm7 Ebm7 Ab Db/F Gb
Say you need me with you, here be - side you, an- y- where you go, let me go
a tempo
Db/Ab Ebm7/Ab Ab6 Ebm7/Ab Db Bbm7
rit.
molto rit.
CHRISTINE
too. Christ- ine, that's all I ask of you.
Say you'll share with me one
f
Ebm7 Ab Db/F Bbm7 Ebm7 Ab Ab7
love, one life- time; say the word and I will fol- low you.
Db Bbm7 Ebm7 Ab Db/F Gb
TOGETHER
CHRISTINE
RAOUL
8va bassa
rit.
Share each day with me, each night, each morn- ing. Say you love me!
You know I

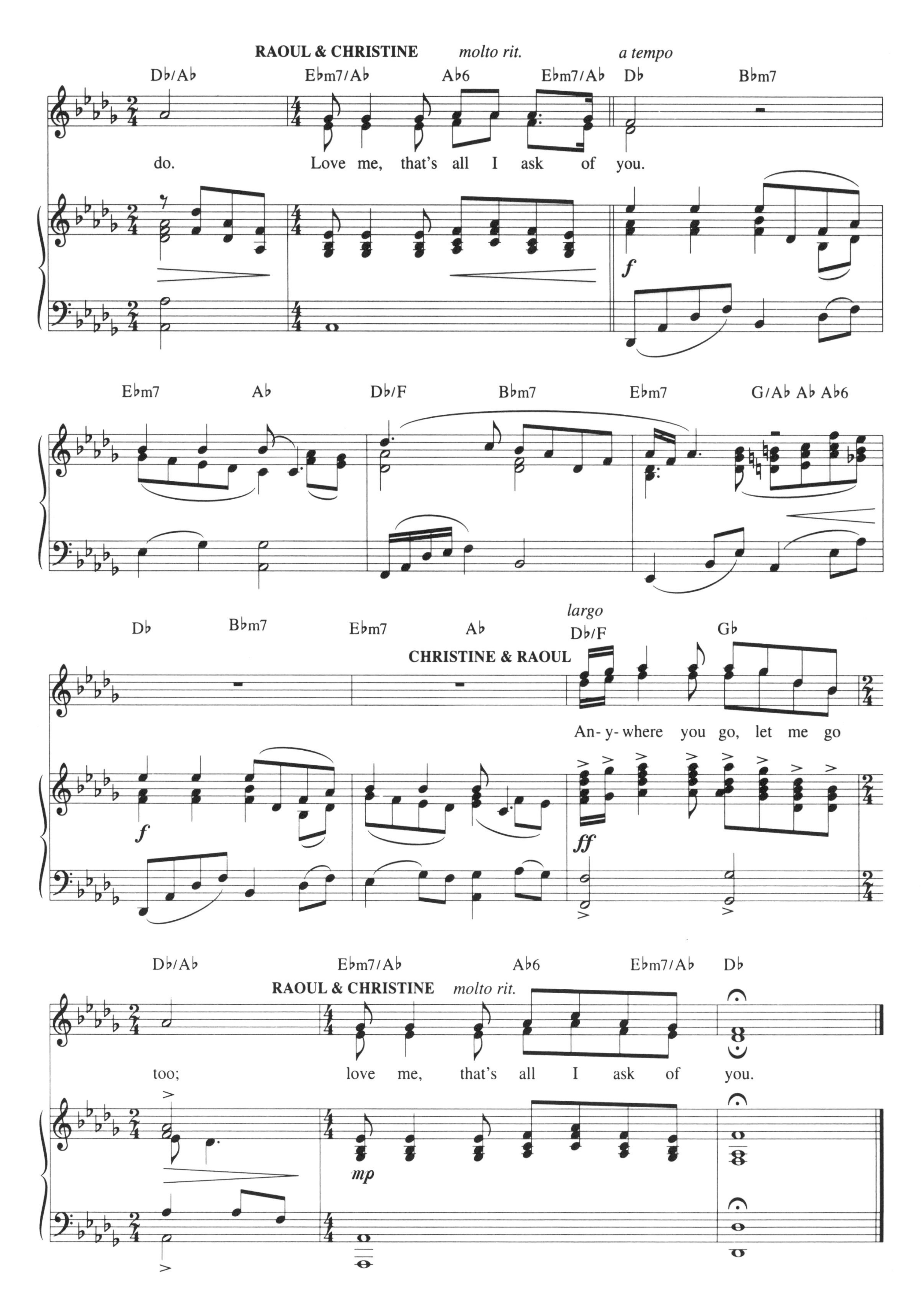
RAOUL & CHRISTINE
molto rit.
a tempo
Db/Ab
Ebm7/Ab
Ab6
Ebm7/Ab
Db
Bbm7
do.
Love me, that's all I ask of you.
f
Ebm7
Ab
Db/F
Bbm7
Ebm7
G/Ab Ab Ab6
Db
Bbm7
Ebm7
Ab
largo
Db/F
Gb
CHRISTINE & RAOUL
An-y-where you go, let me go
f
ff
Db/Ab
Ebm7/Ab
Ab6
Ebm7/Ab
Db
RAOUL & CHRISTINE
molto rit.
too;
love me, that's all I ask of you.
mp

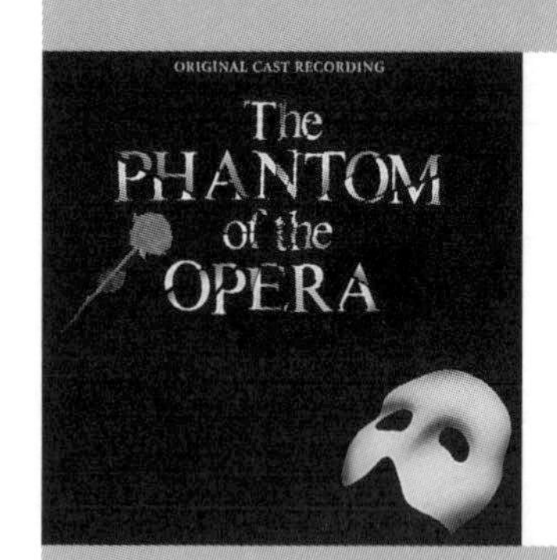

The PHANTOM of the OPERA

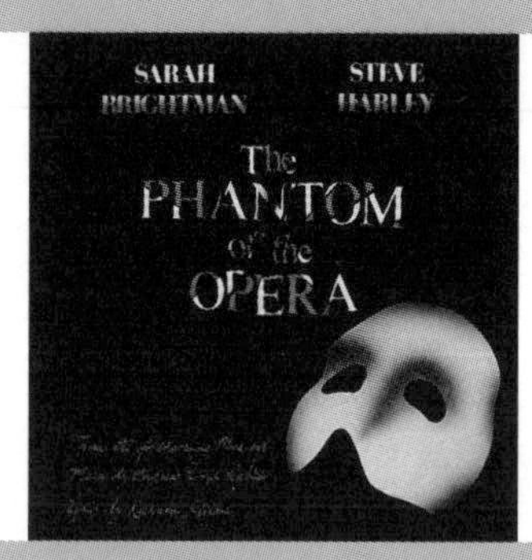

The PHANTOM of the OPERA

THE MUSIC OF THE NIGHT

MUSIC BY ANDREW LLOYD WEBBER
LYRICS BY CHARLES HART
ADDITIONAL LYRICS BY RICHARD STILGOE

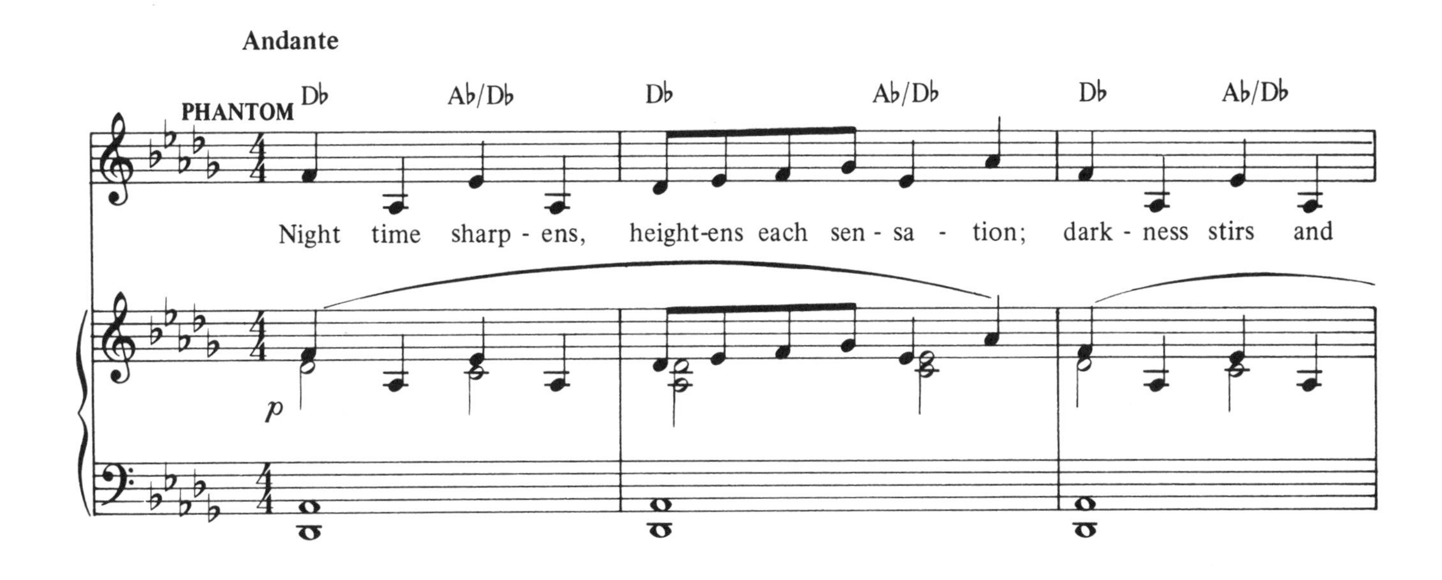
Andante
PHANTOM
Db Ab/Db Db Ab/Db Db Ab/Db
Night time sharp - ens, height-ens each sen - sa - tion; dark - ness stirs and
p

Gb/Db Ab/Db Gb Db Gb Db
wakes im - ag - in - a - tion. Si - lent - ly the sen - ses a - ban - don their de - fen - ces.

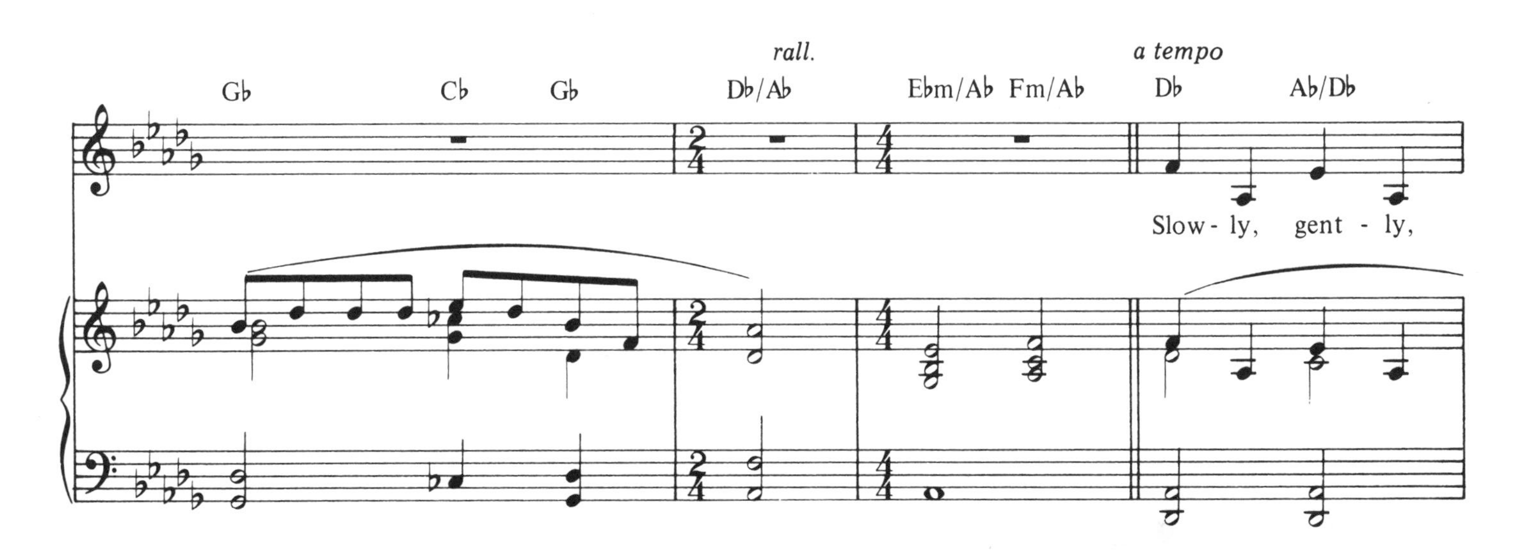
rall.
a tempo
Gb Cb Gb Db/Ab Ebm/Ab Fm/Ab Db Ab/Db
Slow - ly, gent - ly,

Db Ab/Db Db Ab/D Gb Ab
night un - furls its splen - dour; grasp it, sense it, trem - u - lous and ten - der.
Gb Db Gb Db Gb Cb Gb
Turn your face a - way from the gar-ish light of day, turn your thoughts a-way from cold, un - feel - ing
Db/Ab Gb/Ab Ab7 Db B
light and lis-ten to the mu-sic of the night. Close your eyes and sur-ren-der to your
mp
E A Eb Eb7
dark - est dreams! Purge your thoughts of the life you knew be - fore! Close your

Ab Ab7 Db Fm C F
rall.
rit.
eyes let your spi-rit start to soar and you'll live as you've nev-er lived be - fore.
mp
a tempo
Db Ab/Db Db Ab/Db Db Ab/Db
Soft - ly, deft - ly, mu - sic shall ca - ress you. Hear it, feel it,
p
Gb Ab Gb Db Gb Db
se - cret - ly po - ssess you. O - pen up your mind let your fan - ta - sies un-wind in this
Gb Cb Gb Db/Ab Gb/Ab Ab7
rall.
dark-ness which you know you can - not fight, the dark-ness of the mu-sic of the

a tempo
Db
B
E
night. Let your mind start a jour-ney through a strange, new world; leave all
f
A
Eb
rall.
Ab
Ab7
thoughts of the world you knew be - fore. Let your soul take you where you long to
Db
molto rit.
Fm
C
F
be! On - ly then can you be - long to me.
ff
mp
a tempo
Db
Ab/Db
Db
Ab/Db
Db
Ab/Db
Gb/Db
Ab/Db
Float-ing, fall-ing, sweet in-tox-i-ca-tion. Touch me, trust me, sa-vour each sen-sa-tion.
mp

Gb Db Gb Db Gb Cb Gb Db/Ab
Let the dream be-gin, let your dark-er side give in to the pow-er of the mu-sic that I write, the
mf
rall. a tempo
Gb/Ab Ab7 Db Ab/Db Db Ab/Db Db Ab/Db
pow-er of the mu-sic of the night.
ff
rall a tempo poco rit.
Gb Ab7 Gb Db Gb Db Gb Cb Gb
You a-lone can make my song take
mf
rall. lento
Db/Ab Gb/Ab Ab7 Gb Ebm Dm C Db
flight, help me make the mu-sic of the night.
8va
mp pp

LOVE CHANGES EVERYTHING

MUSIC BY ANDREW LLOYD WEBBER
LYRICS BY DON BLACK & CHARLES HART

A A/C♯ D A/E E7
sum - mer fly or a night seem like a life - time. Yes
world a - round and that world will last for ev - er. Yes
A E7 A E7 A E
love, love chan - ges ev - ery - thing: now I trem - ble at your
love, love chan - ges ev - ery - thing, brings you glo - ry, brings you
A D D/E E7
name. No - thing in the world will ev - er be the
shame. No - thing in the world will ev - er be the
cresc.
1. A D/A A
same.
2. A A/G
same.
f
cresc.

D/F♯
Bm7
A/E
Esus4
E
ff
Ped.
Ped.
B♭
F
B♭
F
B♭
E♭
B♭
E♭/B♭
Off ___ in-to the world we go, plan-ning fu-tures, shap-ing years.
f
B♭
F
B♭
F
B♭
E♭
B♭
poco ritard.
Love ___ bursts in and sud-den-ly, all our wis-dom dis-ap-pears.
a tempo
F
F7
B♭
E♭
Love ___ makes fools of ev - ery-one: all the rules we make are

Bb/F F F7 Bb F Bb F
bro - ken. Yes love, love chan - ges ev - ery - thing. Live or
a tempo
Bb F Bb poco ritard. Eb Eb/F F7
per - ish in its flame. Love will nev - er, nev - er let you be the
cresc.
ff
rall.
Bb Bb/Ab Eb/G Eb/F F7
same. Love will nev - er, nev - er let you be the
cresc.
fff
a tempo, meno mosso
molto rall.
Bb F7/Bb Bb F7/Bb Bb Eb/F Bb
same.
dim.
f cresc.

ANY DREAM WILL DO

MUSIC BY ANDREW LLOYD WEBBER
LYRICS BY TIM RICE

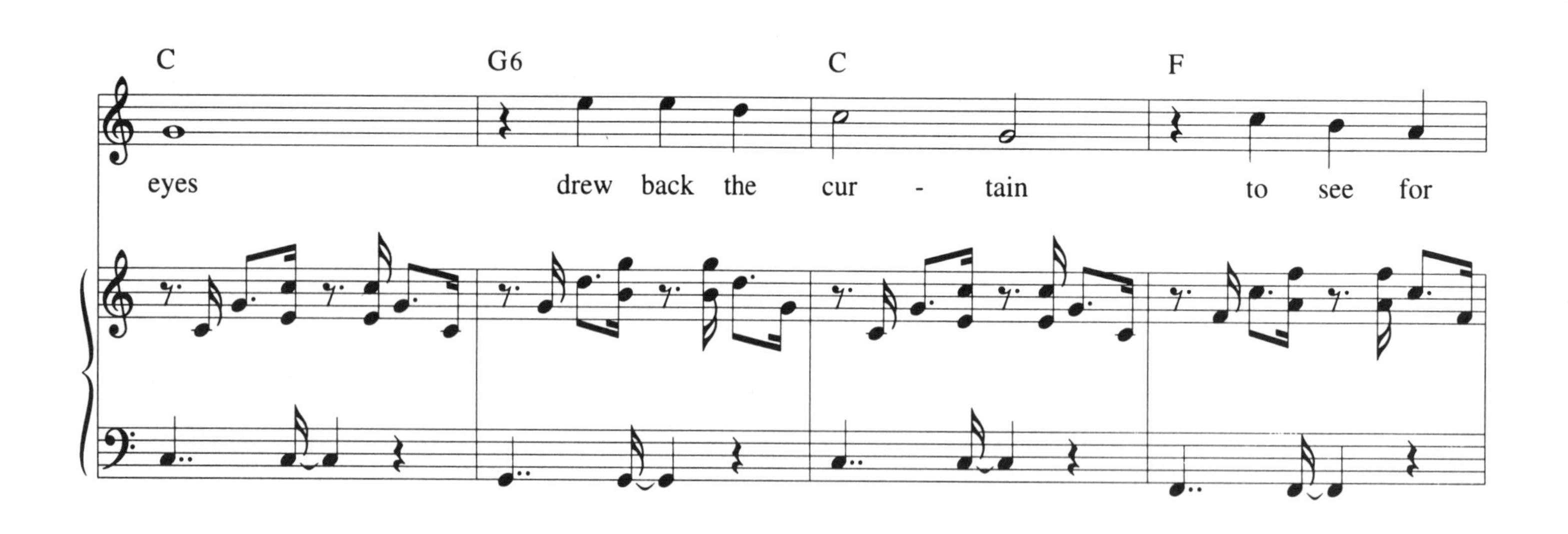

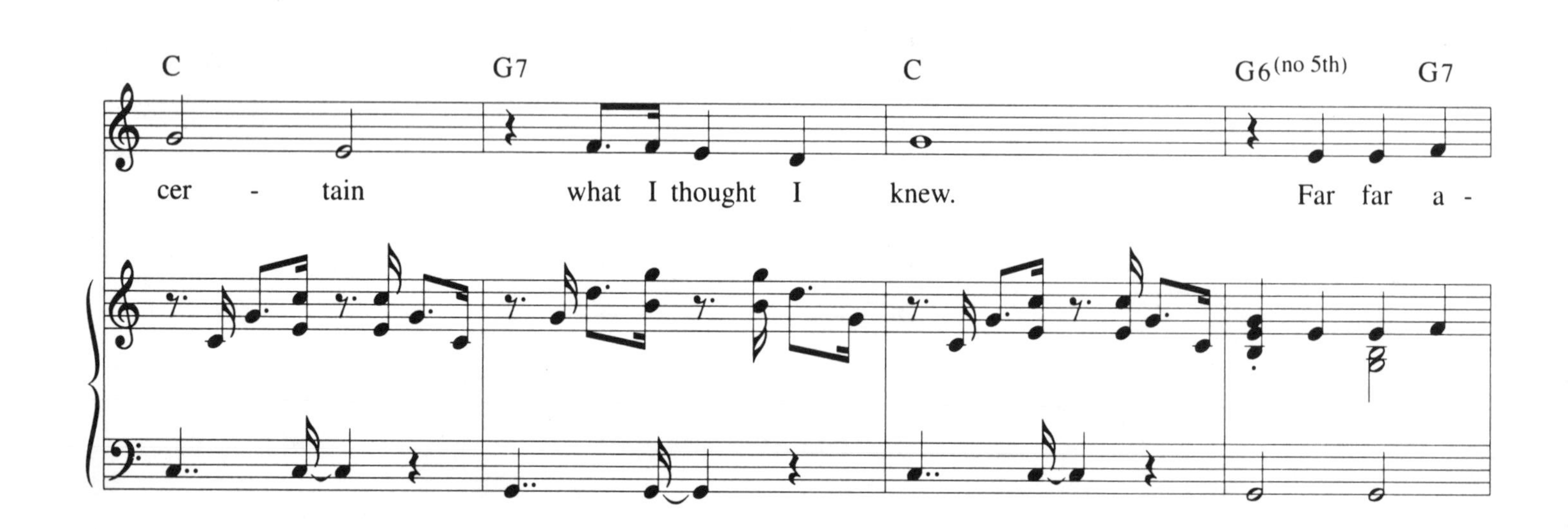

C
G6
C
F
way
some - one was
weep - ing,
but the world was

C
G7
C
G6 (no 5th)
G7
sleep - ing,
a - ny dream will
do.
I wore my

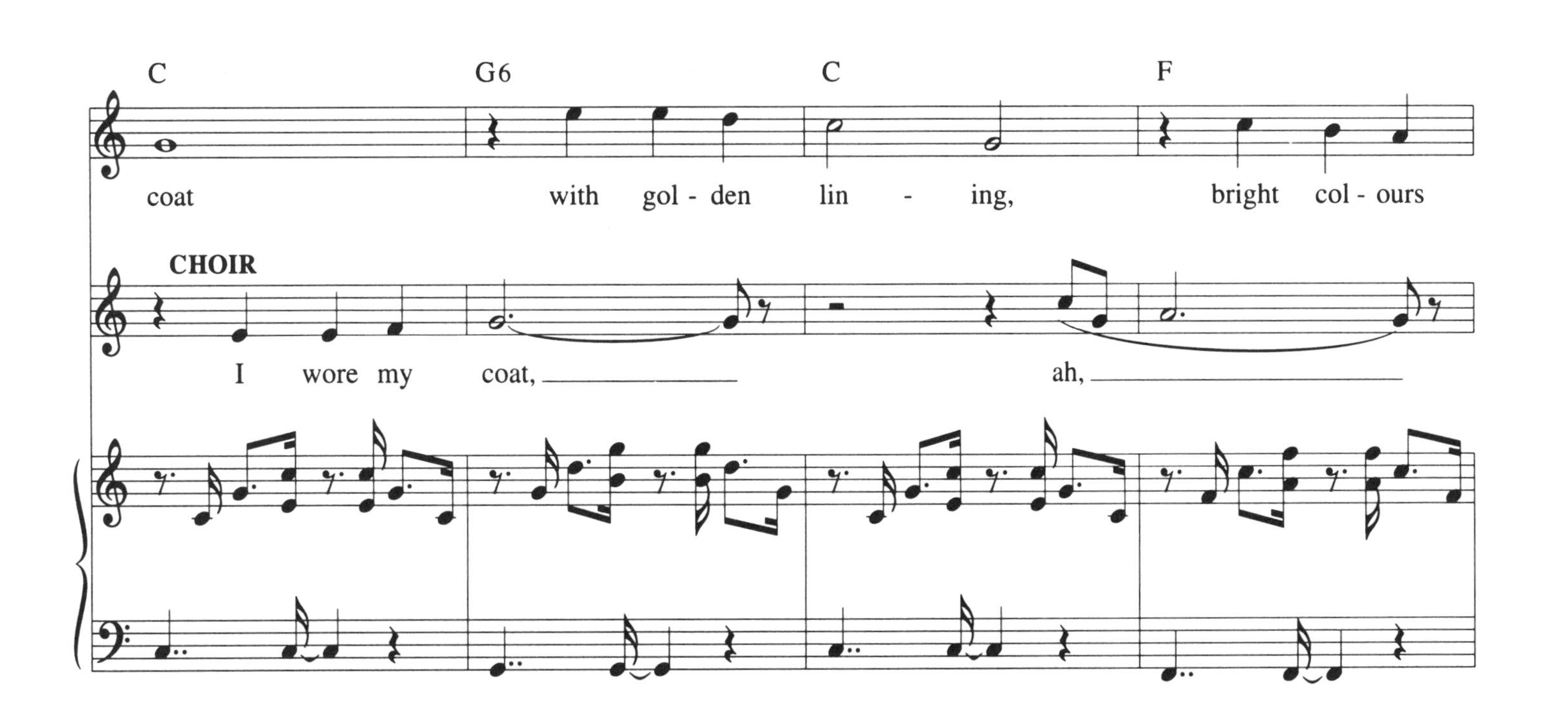
C
G6
C
F
coat
with gol - den
lin - ing,
bright col - ours
CHOIR
I wore my
coat,
ah,

C
G7
C
G6 (no 5th)
G7
shin - ing won- der- ful and new. And in the
ah,

C
G6
C
F
east the dawn was break - ing, and the world was
and in the east,
ah,

C
G7
C
B♭/C
C7
JOSEPH
wak - ing, an - y dream will do.
A
ah.

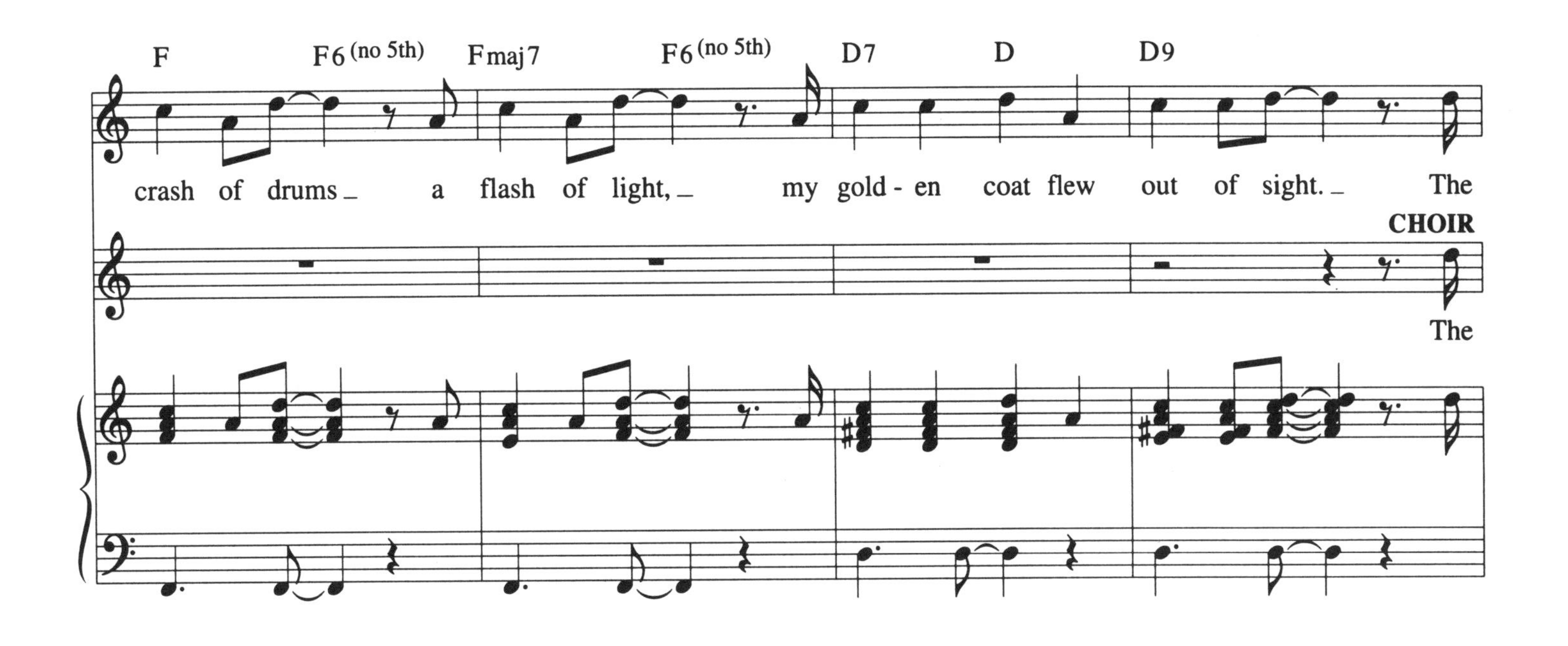
F F6(no 5th) Fmaj7 F6(no 5th) D7 D D9
crash of drums _ a flash of light, _ my gold - en coat flew out of sight. _ The
CHOIR
The

C/G G C G7 C/G G7 C/G G Dm/G G D7/G G
col - ours fad - ed in - to dark - ness, I was left a - lone.
col - ours fad - ed in - to dark - ness, ah, ah,

Dm7/G G7 C G6
May I re - turn, to the be -
ah. May I re - turn,

C
F
C
G7
gin - ning,
the light is
dim - ming
and the dream is
ah,
ah.

C
G6 (no 5th)
G7
C
G6
too,
the world and
I,
we are still
The world and
I,

C
F
C
G
wait - ing,
still he - si - ta - ting
a - ny dream will
ah,
ah.

C
Dm7/C
C
do,
A - ny dream,
a - ny dream will,
a - ny dream,

Dm7/C
C
Dm7/C
a - ny dream will do,
a - ny dream will do, a - ny dream,
a - ny dream will,

C
Dm/G
C
rall.
a - ny dream will do.
a - ny dream,
a - ny dream will do.
rall.

AMIGOS PARA SIEMPRE (FRIENDS FOR LIFE)

MUSIC BY ANDREW LLOYD WEBBER
LYRICS BY DON BLACK

13
Gm/F
B♭m/F
F
mood I'm go - ing through
Feel as though I've known you for e - ver
have - n't start - ed yet
Some-thing hap - pens when we're to - ge - ther
16
You can look in - to my eyes and
When I look at you I won - der
19
Gm/F
see the way I feel and how the world is treat - ing me
why there has to come a time when we must say good - bye
22
B♭m6/F
F
May - be I have known you for - e - ver.
I'm a - live when we are to - ge - ther.
A- MI-GOS PA-RA

25
B♭
C9
F
SIEM-PRE means you'll al-ways be my friend
A - MI - GOS PA - RA SIEM-PRE means a love that can-not
28
Dm7
Gm
C7
end
Friends for life not just a sum-mer or a spring
A - MI - GOS PA - RA
31
B♭
F
B♭
SIEM - PRE
I feel you near me e - ven when we are a -
34
C9
F
Dm7
part
Just know-ing you are in this world can warm my
heart
Friends for

37
Gm
C7
B♭
life not just a sum-mer or a spring A - MI - GOS PA - RA SIEM - PRE.
1.
2.
40
F
F
Maestoso
A♭
f
43
A♭m7
46
B♭m/A♭
D♭m/A♭
A♭

49
When I look at you I won - der
52
Abmaj7
Bbm/Ab
why there has to come a time when we must say good - bye
55
Dbm/Ab
Ab
rallentando
I'm a - live when we are to - ge - ther
A - MI-GOS PA-RA
a tempo
58
Db
Eb9
Ab
SIEM-PRE means you'll al - ways be my friend
A - MI-GOS PA-RA
SIEM-PRE means a love that can-not

61
Fm7
Bbm7
Eb7
end Friends for life not just a sum-mer or a spring A - MI-GOS PA - RA
64
Db
Ab
Db
SIEM - PRE. I feel you near me e - ven when we are a -
67
Eb9
Ab
Fm7
part Just know - ing you are in this world can warm my heart Friends for
70
Bbm
Eb7
Db
life not just a sum - mer or a spring A - MI-GOS PA - RA SIEM - PRE

molto rall.
meno mosso
73
Ab
Db
Eb9
A - MI-GOS PA-RA SIEM-PRE means you'll al - ways be my friend A - MI - GOS PA-RA
76
Ab
F7
SIEM - PRE means a love that can - not end friends for
78
Bbm
Eb7
Db
life not just a sum - mer or a spring A - MI - GOS PA - RA SIEM - PRE A -
81
rall. molto al fine
Ab
MI - GOS PA - RA SIEM - PRE.
ff

THE PERFECT YEAR

MUSIC BY ANDREW LLOYD WEBBER
LYRICS BY DON BLACK & CHRISTOPHER HAMPTON

B♭m
Dm
Dm/B
F/C
C7
ev-ery-thing I want is here, if you're with me, next year will be the per-fect
F
JOE
F
C7♭9/F
F
year. Be-fore we play some dan-gerous game, be-fore we fan some harm-less
B♭/F
Gm
Gm7
C7
flame, we have to ask if this is wise, and if the game is worth the
F
F7
B♭
B♭m
prize. With this wine, and with this mu - sic, how can a - ny-thing be

Dm Dm/B F C7 F
clear? Let's wait and see, it may just be the per-fect year.

C7/F F B♭

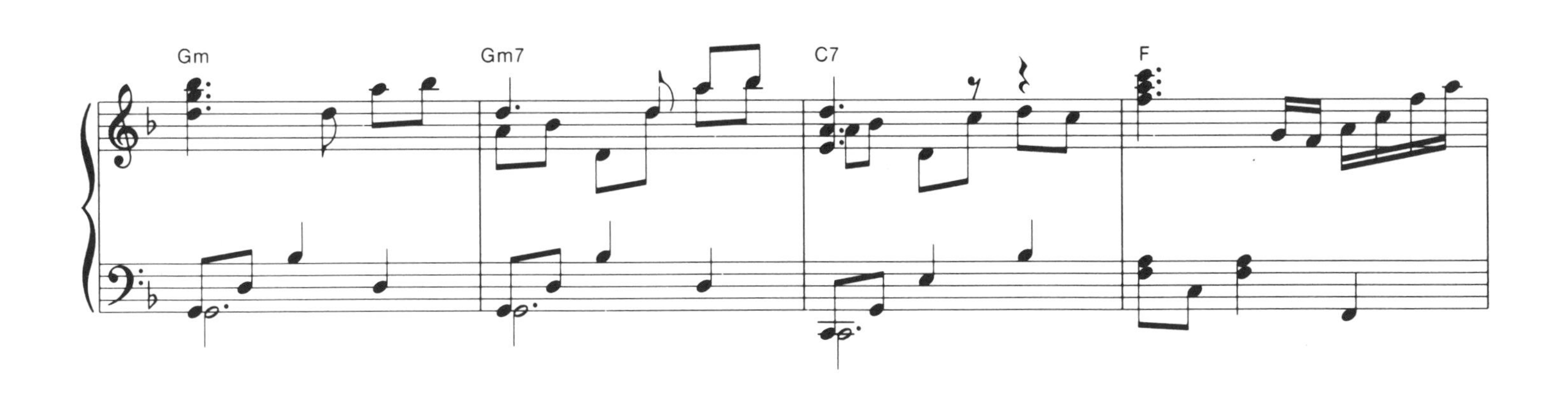
Gm Gm7 C7 F

F7 B♭ B♭m Dm

F/C
C7
F
accel.
F7
f

B♭
B♭m
Dm
Dm/B
F/C

C7
rit.
D♭
NORMA
D♭7
G♭
D♭7/G♭
It's New Year's Eve, and hopes are high, dance one year
pp

G♭
C♭
A♭m
A♭m7
in, kiss one good - bye, an - oth - er chance, an - oth - er start, so ma - ny

D♭7
G♭
G♭7
C♭
dreams to tease the heart.
We don't need a crowd - ed ball - room,
C♭m
E♭m
A♭7/C
G♭/D♭
D♭7
ev-ery-thing we want is here, and face to face we will em - brace the per-fect
G♭
G♭7
C♭
C♭m
year.
We don't need a crowd - ed ball - room,
ev-ery-thing we want is
E♭m
A♭7/C
G♭/D♭
ritenuto
D♭7
G♭
here, and face to face we will em - brace the per-fect year.

AS IF WE NEVER SAID GOODBYE

MUSIC BY ANDREW LLOYD WEBBER
LYRICS BY DON BLACK & CHRISTOPHER HAMPTON
WITH CONTRIBUTIONS BY AMY POWERS

Fm/E♭
E♭
E♭maj7
D♭maj7
ov-er-crowd-ed hall-ways, the at-mos-phere as thrill-ing here as al - ways.
L.H.
A♭/C
Fm7
Feel the ear-ly morn-ing mad - ness, feel the ma-gic in the mak - ing. Why,
E♭maj7/B♭
A♭/B♭
E♭
ev-ery-thing's as if we ne - ver said good - bye. I've
mf
E♭maj7
Fm/E♭
E♭
spent so ma-ny morn-ings, just try-ing to re-sist you. I'm trem-bling now, you

E♭maj7
D♭maj7
A♭/C
can't know how_ I've missed you,_ missed the fai-ry tale ad-ven-tures_ in this
Fm7
D♭
A♭/C
B♭7
ev-er-spin-ning play-ground._ We were young to-geth-er, I'm
E♭maj7
A♭/E♭
E♭
com-ing out of make-up, the light's al-rea-dy burn-ing,_ not long un-til_ the
f
E♭maj7
D♭maj7
A♭/C
cam-eras will_ start turn-ing,_ and the ear-ly morn-ing mad-ness,_

Fm
Ebmaj7/Bb
and the ma-gic in the mak - ing,
yes, ev-ery-thing's as if we
Fm7/Bb
Eb
molto accel.
Gm7
Cm7
ne - ver said good - bye.
I don't want to be a - lone,
Gm7
Cm7
Bb
Cm
Gm
Cm
that's all in the past.
This world's wait - ed long e - nough,
I've come home at
Bb7
Ebmaj7
Ab/Eb
last,
and this time will be big - ger,
and bright-ter than we knew it.
f assai

E♭
E♭maj7
D♭maj7
So watch me fly, we all know I can do it. Could I
A♭/C
Fm7
stop my hand from shak - ing? Has there ev - er been a mo - ment with so
D♭
A♭/C
B♭7
E♭maj7
much to live for? The whis-pered con - ver - sa - tions in
p
Fm/E♭
E♭
E♭maj7
ov - er-crowd-ed hall - ways, so much to say, not just to - day, but

D♭maj7
A♭/C
al - ways.
We'll have
ear-ly morn-ing mad - ness,
we'll have
f
L.H.
Fm
E♭maj7/B♭
A♭6/B♭
ma-gic in the mak - ing,
yes,
ev-ery-thing's as if we
ne - ver said good -
Cm
Cm/A
E♭maj7/B♭
A♭6/B♭
B♭7
E♭
D♭/E♭
- bye,
yes,
ev-ery-thing's as if we
ne - ver said good - bye.
A♭
B♭sus4
E♭
B♭
A♭/E♭
E♭
We taught the world
new ways to
dream.
mp
f

YOU MUST LOVE ME

MUSIC BY ANDREW LLOYD WEBBER
LYRICS BY TIM RICE

♩= 92
B♭
F/B♭
B♭
B♭
B♭7
Where do we go from here? This is - n't where we in -
colla voce–accompaniment optional
E♭
fr3
Cm7
fr3
tend - ed to be. We had it all, you be - lieved in me, I be -
(play)
F11
F
F11
F
lieved in you.

B♭
F/B♭
B♭
Cer - tain - ties dis - ap - pear
(2º see block lyric)
B♭7
E♭
fr3
what do we do for our dream to sur - vive,
Cm7
fr3
F11
F
how do we keep all our pas-sions a - live as we used to do?
F11
F
D7
Gm
fr3
3
Deep in my heart I'm con - ceal - ing
3

D7
Gm
fr3
D7
things that I'm long - ing to say,
scared to con - fess what I'm
rit.
F/E♭
E♭
Cm7
Dm7
F
3
feel - ing
fright - ened you'll slip a - way,
you must love
a tempo
B♭
E♭/B♭
F/B♭
me,
you must love
To Coda
B♭
E♭/B♭
F/B♭
B♭
F/B♭
me.

2° lyric
Why are you at my side?
How can I be any use to you now?
Give me a chance and I'll let you see how
Nothing has changed.
Deep in my heart I'm concealing
Things that I'm longing to say,
Scared to confess what I'm feeling
Frightened you'll slip away,
You must love me.

WHISTLE DOWN THE WIND

MUSIC BY ANDREW LLOYD WEBBER
LYRICS BY JIM STEINMAN

D
Dmaj7
D6
Dsus2
D
Dmaj7
D6
Whist - le down the wind,
let your voi - ces car - ry
A7/D
D
drown out all the rain,
light a patch of dark - ness,
treach - er - ous and sca - ry.
D6
D
Dmaj7
D6
D
Howl at the stars,
whis - per when you're sleep - ing.
mp

A7/D
Dsus2
D
I'll be there to hold you, I'll be there to stop the chills and all the weep- ing. Make it

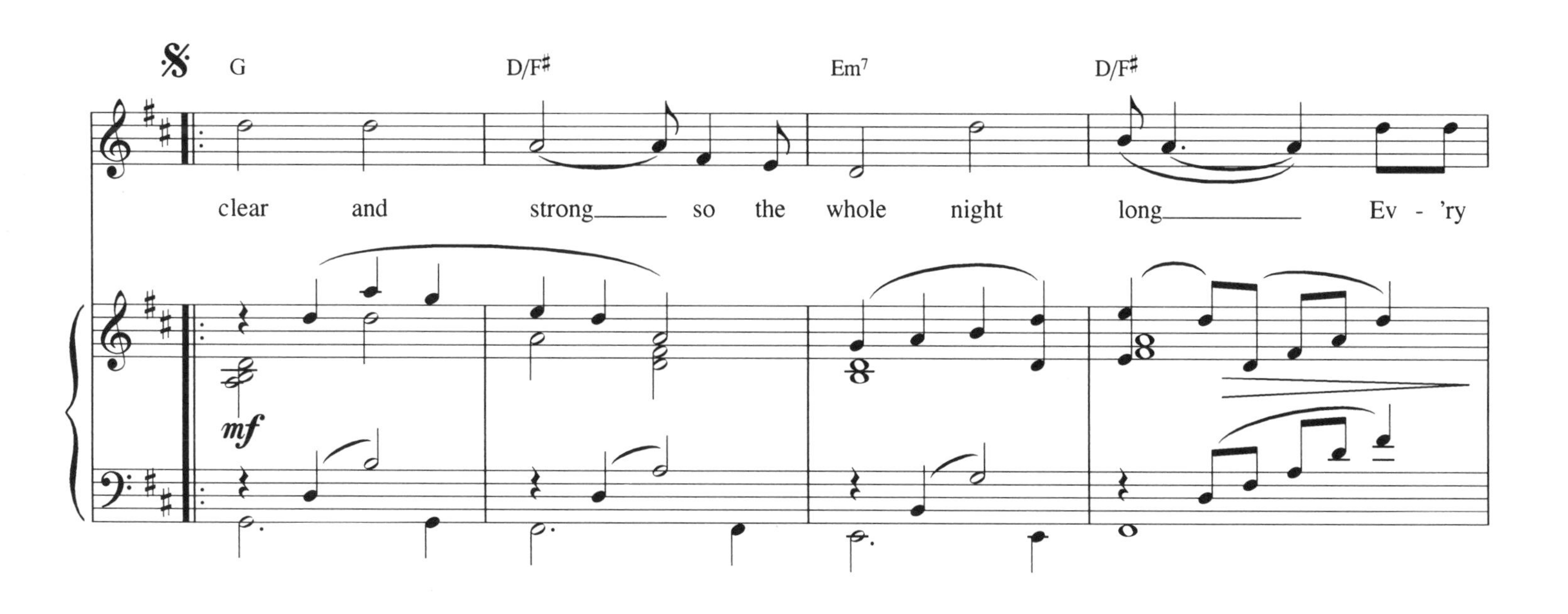
G
D/F♯
Em7
D/F♯
clear and strong so the whole night long Ev - 'ry
mf

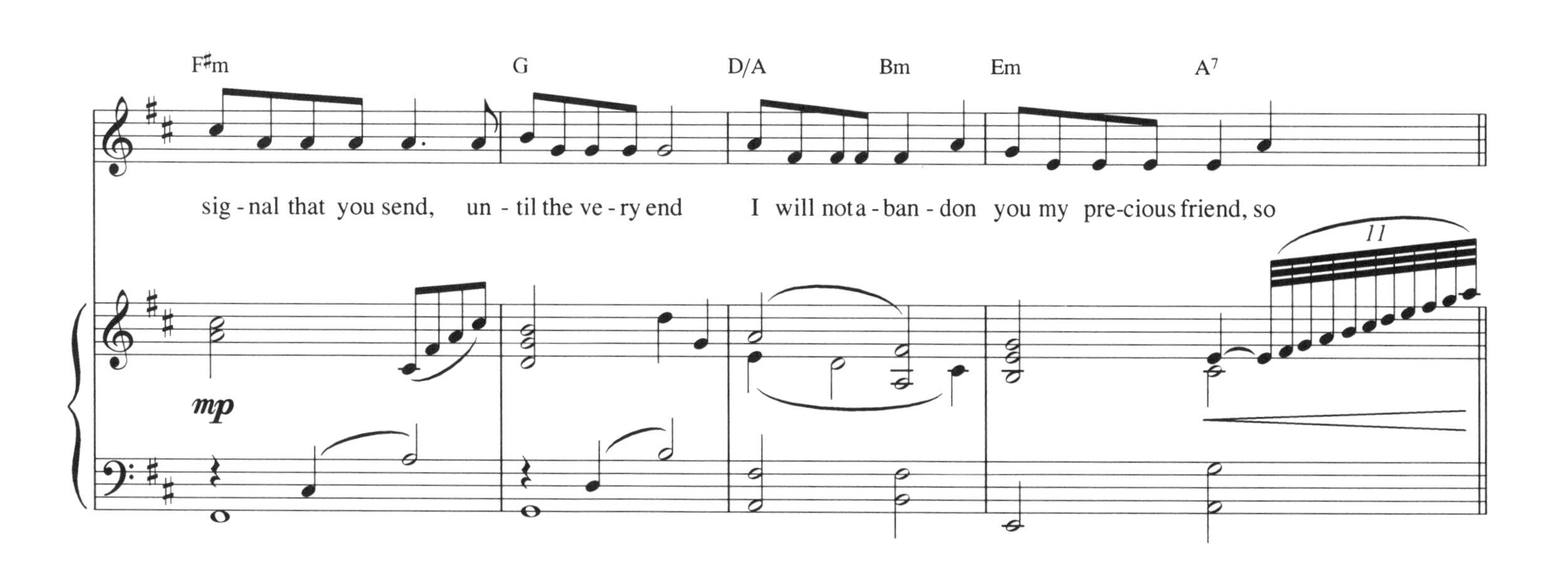
F♯m
G
D/A
Bm
Em
A7
sig - nal that you send, un - til the ve - ry end I will not a - ban - don you my pre-cious friend, so
mp
11

Dsus2
D
Dmaj7
D6
Dsus2
D
try and stem the tide
then you'll raise a ban - ner
send a
f

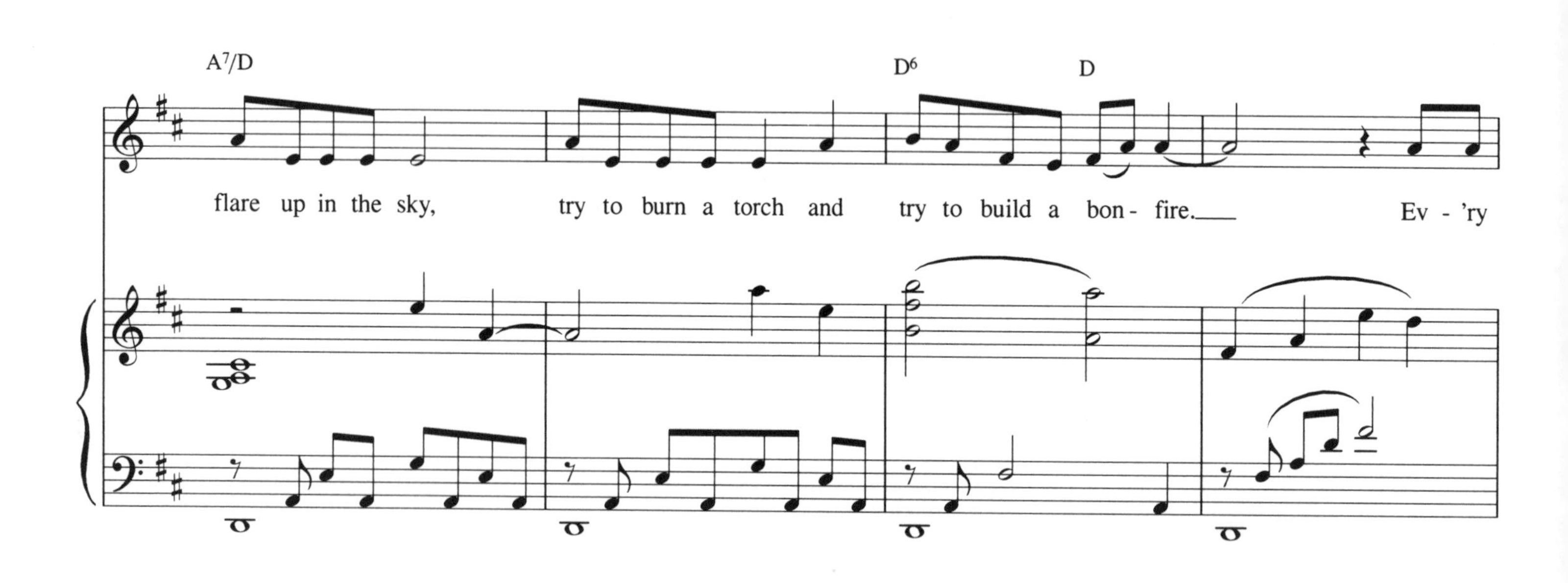
A7/D
D6
D
flare up in the sky,
try to burn a torch and
try to build a bon - fire.
Ev - 'ry

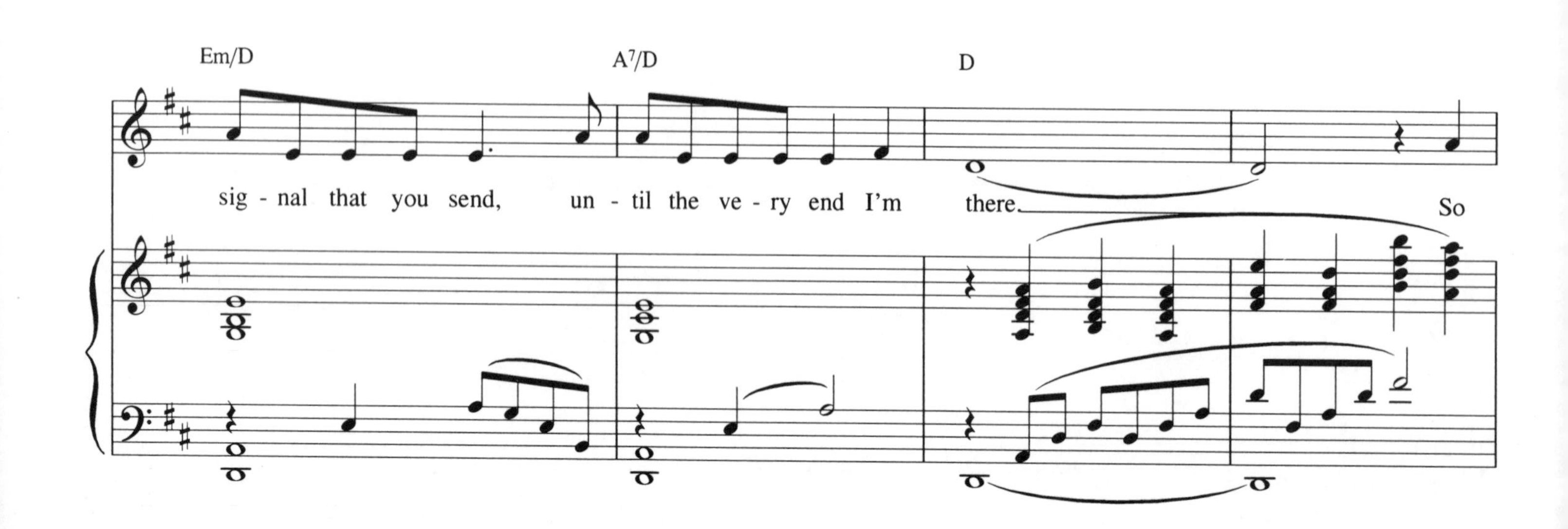
Em/D
A7/D
D
sig - nal that you send,
un - til the ve - ry end I'm
there.
So

1.
A7/D
D
D6
D
Dmaj7
D6
whis - tle down the wind for I have al ways been right here.
(1.)
D6
D
Dmaj7
D6
A7/D
Dmaj7
D7
Make it
2.
A7/D
D
whis - tle down the wind for I have al - ways been right there.
p

NO MATTER WHAT

MUSIC BY ANDREW LLOYD WEBBER
LYRICS BY JIM STEINMAN

A
No mat - ter what they call us, how - ev - er they at -
No mat - ter what they tell you, no mat - ter what they
Bm/A
Bm
D/E E
- tack, no mat - ter where they take us,
do, no mat - ter what they teach you,
Esus4
E
A
we'll find our own way back.
what you be - lieve is true.
I can't de - ny what I
And I will keep you safe
A7
D
believe, I can't be what I'm not.
and strong and shel - tered from the storm.

Bm
D/E
E
E sus4
E7
I know our love's for - ev - er,
I know no mat - ter what.
No mat - ter where it's bar - ren
our dream is be - ing born.
1.
2.
A
A
C
f Instrumental
Dm
Dm/G
G7
G
C
F/C

C
F/C
C
Dm
No mat-ter who they fol-low,
no mat-ter where they lead,
F/G
G7
Gsus4
G7
no mat-ter how they judge us
I'll be eve-ry one you need.
C
C7/E
No mat-ter if the sun don't shine,
F
C/E
Dm
or if the skies are blue.
No mat-ter what the

F/G G7 Gsus4 G7 C
ending, my life began with you. I
C C7/E F rall. C/E
can't deny what I believe, I can't be what I'm not.
Colla voce
Dm G7
I know this love's for ever, That's all that matters now no matter
a tempo
C2
Repeat to fade
No no matter no. No no matter no.
what. No no mat- ter what. No no mat-